Connect to
NCTM Standards 2000

Making the Standards
Work at Grade 3

Francis (Skip) Fennell, Ph.D.

Honi J. Bamberger, Ph.D.

Thomas E. Rowan, Ph.D.

Kay B. Sammons

Anna R. Suarez

Creative Publications®
A Tribune Education Company

Acknowledgments

Project Editors → Diane Nieker, Jeff Stiegel

Writers → Tim Burnett, Marilyn Davis, Beth Sycamore

Writing and Editorial Services → MathLink, Inc.

Design Director → Karen Stack

Design → Gerta Sorensen-London

Project Coordinator → Barbara Quincer

Cover Illustration → Jim Dandy

Illustrators → Susan Aiello, Jim Dandy, Sarah Frederking

Production → Graphic Advantage, Ltd.

Manufacturing → Dallas Richards

© 2000 Creative Publications®, Inc.
Two Prudential Plaza
Chicago, IL 60601

This is an independent publication and is not affiliated with, or sponsored by, the NCTM. The NCTM 2000 Standards are not reproduced in this book. This book is designed to be read independently of the *Principles and Standards for School Mathematics* and to aid educators in preparing to teach in a manner consistent with the *Principles and Standards*.

ISBN 0-7622-1245-4
Catalog No. 21308
Customer Service 800-624-0822
http://www.creativepublications.com
1 2 3 4 5 6 7 8 MAL 05 04 03 02 01 00

Contents

Overview

Since *Curriculum and Evaluation Standards for School Mathematics* was released in 1989, much has been learned about how ideas work in the classroom and how students learn mathematics. The release of the *Principles and Standards for School Mathematics* creates an opportunity for us to examine our goals, our math curricula, and our teaching methods in light of these new insights and to consider practices and procedures that will improve school mathematics education. As did the original draft, *Principles and Standards* promotes ways for all educators to strengthen the teaching and learning of mathematics by addressing two important concerns: the characteristics of instructional programs that will provide high-quality mathematical experiences for students as they progress through school, and the mathematical content and processes students should know and use as they advance from grade to grade.

General Overview

Connect to NCTM Standards 2000 is designed to help you understand and implement the NCTM standards. Regardless of your teaching style, the information presented in this book will help you to make the standards work. *Principles and Standards* identifies ten standards. Five of those standards are described as content standards that organize all of mathematics into five broad areas of learning; they address *what* students learn. The other five standards, the process standards, are concerned with *how* students learn and how information is presented.

Today, more than ever, there is a need for all students to have a strong base in mathematics. This means that students do not just memorize facts and procedures, but that they have an understanding of mathematics and mathematical thinking. The interplay between content and process is complicated, but integrating the two is critical if our students are to receive the mathematics education they will need to function effectively in the world they will grow into.

The lessons contained within *Connect to NCTM Standards 2000* are organized into sections by content. Each section contains four lessons dealing with some aspect of that content standard. Each lesson demonstrates ways to develop the content by using the process standards. An overview highlights grade-level content skills and gives a brief description of the four lessons for that standard.

Content Standards

Number and Operation

Algebra

Geometry

Measurement

Data Analysis and Probability

Process Standards

Problem Solving

Reasoning and Proof

Communication

Connections

Representation

The last section of the book, entitled Create Your Own Lesson, is designed to help you develop lessons of your own that will comfortably incorporate the NCTM standards with your teaching style.

About the Lessons

Each content standard section contains four lessons that address some aspect of the content at the grade level. Three of the lessons have been specially developed to model ways the process standards can be used to develop the content being presented. The fourth lesson examines a hypothetical math textbook lesson in terms of how the process standards are incorporated into that lesson. Suggestions are offered for increasing the focus on three of the five process standards to create a more effective lesson. Then, a lesson is presented modeling how those suggestions can be implemented.

As you read through the lessons, keep in mind that what is offered is only one possible approach. You might have a completely different idea about how to develop the concept, and that's fine. These lessons are intended to provide examples of how the process standards can work to make mathematics lessons more meaningful, and to model questions and techniques that you might incorporate into your teaching. As you read through the lessons, pay attention to how the process standards are being used. Use the ideas presented as a springboard for your own ideas.

Each lesson is intended for a single class period. Some introduce a concept, others require that students have some experience with the concept, and still others are meant to be used at the end of a unit. As you examine these lessons, think about how and where they fit into your curriculum. Any of the lessons here can be used as a replacement for the comparable lesson in your current math program. Try the lessons and see the difference incorporating the process standards can make.

Creating Your Own Lessons

The last section of the book is designed to help you develop lessons of your own that incorporate the NCTM standards and are compatible with your teaching style. You will find questions to help you focus on ideas to consider as you begin to organize a standards-based lesson. You will also have an opportunity to follow the thoughts and decisions one person used in the process of developing a lesson.

About the Authors

Francis (Skip) Fennell, Ph.D.

Dr. Fennell was a member of the writing team of *Principles and Standards for School Mathematics* (NCTM, 2000). He has authored mathematics textbooks, materials for both students and teachers, and numerous articles for leading mathematics journals. Dr. Fennell has served on the Board of Directors of NCTM and as Program Officer of instructional materials and teacher enhancement within the Division of Elementary, Secondary, and Informal Education at the National Science Foundation. He has been selected as Outstanding Mathematics Educator by the Maryland Council of Teachers of Mathematics, and as Professor of the Year by both the Carnegie Foundation and Western Maryland College, where he is a professor of education.

Honi J. Bamberger, Ph.D.

Dr. Bamberger is a recognized math scholar and teacher. She has taught at both the elementary school and college levels, served as an associate research scientist and mathematics consultant for Johns Hopkins University, and contributed as a consultant and content writer for the "Numbers Alive" public television series. Dr. Bamberger has presented her research findings at mathematics conferences across the country, and has been an author for a number of mathematics textbooks. Currently, Dr. Bamberger is executive director of Insight, a consulting firm specializing in professional development in mathematics education.

Thomas E. Rowan, Ph.D.

Dr. Rowan was a member of the working group that wrote the K–4 section of the *Curriculum and Evaluation Standards for School Mathematics*. Since the Standards were first published, he has worked with many school systems to help bring about the transition to standards-based classroom mathematics instruction in grades K–8. Dr. Rowan is a frequent presenter at NCTM and author of mathematics texts and numerous articles on teaching and learning mathematics. He currently teaches at the University of Maryland where he focuses on methods of teaching elementary school mathematics.

Kay B. Sammons

Kay Sammons is currently Elementary Mathematics Supervisor for the Howard County Public Schools in Ellicott City, Maryland, where she is responsible for curriculum and staff development for elementary teachers. She is a frequent presenter at state and national mathematics conferences. In addition to serving as a reviewer for NCTM publications, she has written textbooks and teacher resource materials. Ms. Sammons was honored as Elementary Mathematics Teacher of the Year by the Maryland Council Teachers of Mathematics and as Outstanding Educator of the Year by that same organization.

Anna R. Suarez

Anna Suarez is a national consultant and program director for K–8 Mathematics at the National Science Foundation in Arlington, Virginia. Her participation in an NSF-funded research study, Cognitively Guided Instruction (C.G.I.), helped to develop teachers' knowledge of students' mathematical thinking as the basis for making instructional decisions. She has written staff development materials for both the *Investigations* curriculum and Insight.

About the Standards

The *Principles and Standards for School Mathematics 2000* are built around ten curriculum standards. Five of those standards address the mathematical content, or body of mathematical knowledge, that students should learn. Content standards prescribe *what* is to be taught in mathematics. The content standards are Number and Operation, Algebra, Geometry, Measurement, and Data Analysis and Probability.

The other five standards are process standards. The process standards describe *how* the content is delivered. They address how students will acquire the necessary mathematical content and how that knowledge will be applied. The five process standards are identified as Problem Solving, Reasoning and Proof, Communication, Connections, and Representation.

It should be pointed out that the content standards and process standards are not separate subsets of the whole, but are intricately interrelated. How mathematics is learned is as important as what mathematics is learned. The process standards help to "frame" how the content standards are presented.

It is possible to weave the process standards into the teaching of mathematics through a variety of methods. Students can and should be presented with meaningful problems to solve and situations that require them to reason through information to find solutions. They should be asked to defend their solutions and explain their thinking. In presenting a problem to students, connections might be made to a similar problem to build on previous learning. A representative model might be used to enhance students' understanding of a concept. Continuous communication, written and oral, will provide feedback about students' understanding.

For students to become mathematically powerful, it is essential that they be able to use process skills flexibly. They need to practice applying reasoning to solve problems and proving that their solutions are correct. They need to experiment with a variety of representations and have the ability to use them in solving problems and in illustrating their thinking. They should be able to communicate their mathematical thinking and solutions to the teacher and to other students both orally and in writing. Making connections between problems within mathematics is as essential as is making mathematical connections to disciplines outside of mathematics. The importance of how these processes interrelate and work together cannot be overemphasized.

Content Standards

Number and Operation

Algebra

Geometry

Measurement

Data Analysis and Probability

Process Standards

Problem Solving

Reasoning and Proof

Communication

Connections

Representation

Intermediate Problem Solving

PROBLEM SOLVING IS AT THE HEART of mathematics—it is what mathematicians do. Balance is achieved through the interrelationship of conceptual learning, basic skills, and problem solving. Students need to develop concepts with concrete representations to ensure understanding and to build a strong foundation. They need basic skills in order to apply their understandings with efficiency. But most importantly, they need good problems to solve, problems in which they can apply their conceptual understandings and utilize basic skills.

In its simplest form, problem solving means finding a solution when the answer is not readily apparent. Because problem solving does not always follow a uniform plan, students need to develop persistence to be able to work problems through to the end. Sometimes persistence means changing direction. *Well, we know that way doesn't work. What should we try next? Is there another way we can look at this problem?* Questions that encourage students to look for other options should be an integral part of the discussions that take place in mathematics classes.

Choosing problems that have relevance to students is an important factor in creating enthusiasm for problem solving. Often, the enthusiasm of the teacher translates into a positive disposition toward problem solving to students. If statements like, "Now that's an unusual problem. I wonder how we can find the answer," are part of a teacher's repertoire, children get the notion that problem solving is interesting and they are encouraged to use their own resources to find a path to the solution.

Acquiring a variety of strategies to access for problem solving is essential to experiencing success. Having flexibility to solve problems in different ways enables students to get "unstuck" if they reach a "dead end." It allows them to have other approaches to try. Students should be provided with instruction and practice in using a wide range of strategies to draw upon.

When intermediate grade students are presented with a problem which doesn't exactly conform to what has been learned previously, they need to develop strategies based on their skills and concepts.

A fourth grade teacher presented the following problem to the class:

How many different rectangles can you find on your geoboard?
Work with a partner and record your solutions on geoboard dot paper.

Interesting communication ensued between students and teacher from the beginning of the lesson. *What is a rectangle?*

Scott responded, "A shape with four corners."

What is the word that mathematicians use to describe corners?

"They're angles," suggested Kiesha.

What do we know about the angles of a rectangle?

"They are all right angles," Armando stated.

Does anyone know how many degrees are in a right angle?

"Ninety degrees," contributed Ryan.

Show me a rectangle on your geoboard.

The students used their rubber bands to make rectangles on their geoboards. The teacher held up Kristen's geoboard. *What do you think about the shape Kristen found?*

"That's a square, not a rectangle," offered Anna.

"But a square is a rectangle," argued Kristen.

Following a discussion about the properties of rectangles and squares, the students were paired to begin their exploration. The teacher described the parameters of the problem. *Your task today is to find all the different rectangles you can on your geoboard. The rectangles must all be different. If the rectangle is just in a different place or flipped on its side, it doesn't count as being different.*

As the students were discovering and recording their "finds," the teacher checked to make sure there were no duplicates and prompted students to think of ways to create rectangles. *I wonder if you could find a rectangle that is tilted. Would that be different than the straight ones? Can you find a rectangle that is similar to this one, but a little larger?*

After students had found several rectangles, a class discussion was held for students to share their findings. Using an overhead model of a geoboard, different students demonstrated rectangles they had found. As each rectangle was identified, pairs tried to find the same one on their geoboard dot paper. If they were unable to find it, they were directed to construct it on their geoboard and record it on their geoboard dot paper. By the end of the math period, the class had found 15 different rectangles. The teacher let them know that they had done a wonderful job and then closed the lesson with a challenge. *There are 16 possible rectangles. Do you think someone will be able to find the 16th rectangle?*

This engaging problem-solving activity provides an example of how the processes work together in a lesson. Connections were made as students clarified definitions and represented shapes with geoboards and drawings. Communication was woven into all parts of the lesson from the introductory dialogue with the class through the questions posed to students during the exploration to the culminating discussion. Reasoning and proof was involved in identifying and proving that rectangles were different from one another.

Problem solving should be at the core of any mathematics curriculum. Through working well-chosen problems, students are challenged to apply the skills they have learned in new ways that expand their thinking and understanding of concepts. Students who are consistently presented with challenging problems learn to develop and apply new strategies. When they are also given opportunities to communicate their strategies with others and reflect on their thinking, their problem solving abilities are further enhanced.

Intermediate Reasoning and Proof

REASONING IS FUNDAMENTAL TO THE STUDY of mathematics— it is a state of mind that causes students to explore, to justify, and to validate. It permeates all content areas and all grade levels. Students are reasoning when they interpret data, when they solve problems, and when they view geometric patterns and shapes. As they are presented with new problems, they use reasoning skills to apply previously acquired information and to test the validity of their solutions. Reasoning is the process by which students make sense of mathematics.

As they develop mathematically, students learn that mathematics is a discipline based on an inherent set of rules. Reasoning begins with intuition. This intuition is used by the even the youngest children in their efforts to make sense of mathematics, and it should be encouraged as the basis of reasoning at all grade levels. This informal intuition will become the basis for reasoning through representations that are more formal and for proofs based upon the rules.

What are some ways reasoning and proof can be incorporated into the mathematics class? An excellent way is to ask questions that hold students accountable for their thinking. *How did you get your answer? Tell me how you thought about that. Why does your solution work? Do you think that strategy will always work?*

Piaget believed that for children to develop reasoning, it was imperative to have social interaction. A powerful means of achieving this interaction is through mathematical discussions. Designating time during the class for students to put forth their ideas for examination is critical. Students must learn to explain and defend their thinking. They must also learn to detect unsound reasoning in explanations presented by other students. In any given class there will be a wide range of reasoning abilities. It is helpful for students with less mature reasoning to hear from those with well-developed skills. These mathematical discussions increase a student's repertoire of reasoning skills.

What do these mathematical discussions look like? A teacher typically presents a problem to the class that may be related to concepts being studied. Early in the year, before the multiplication algorithm was introduced, the following problem was presented to a fourth grade class.

What is 24 × 6?

After time was allowed for students to solve the problem, they were asked to share their responses.

- The first student reported that the answer was 144.
  When asked by the teacher to explain how he got the answer he said, "I multiplied 20 times 6 and got 120. Then I multiplied 4 × 6 and got 24. I added 120 and 24 and got 144."

- Another student responded, "I got 144 too, but I did it differently." When asked to explain how she got the answer, she responded, "I thought that 24 is close to 25 and 25 is like a quarter. So I thought of 6 quarters and that would be $1.50. But that is too much because there are only 24 and not 25 so I had to subtract 6 from $1.50. I got 144."

- A third student interjected, "I got 144 too, but I did it a different way. I broke 24 into 10 + 10 + 4 because it's easier for me to multiply tens. I multiplied 10 × 6 and got 60. I had to do it twice. I got 120. Then I multiplied the 6 times the 4 and got 24. I added it to the 120 and got 144."

The teacher asked if this third solution was related in any way to the others. One student said, "It's a lot like the first one, but instead of multiplying 20 × 6, 10 was multiplied by 6 and then doubled." Whether a student is explaining his answer to the class or listening to the explanation of another, the time spent on this kind of discussion is invaluable. All students benefit when they are asked to defend their answers as well as to reflect on someone else's solution to determine whether it makes sense.

Intermediate Communication

WHETHER BETWEEN TEACHER AND STUDENT, between a pair of students, or among groups of students, the communication skills of reading, writing, listening, and speaking provide the means for sharing ideas and promoting mathematical understanding. As students express their ideas through oral and written language, they have an opportunity to clarify their thinking and reinforce their own comprehension of the concepts they are working with. By listening to explanations given by their classmates, students are exposed to ideas they may not have thought of. This provides a greater network of connections among ideas and, in turn, enhances learning.

Ample opportunities to discuss mathematical ideas should be provided. One way to promote this is to present an interesting problem to the class, allow time to solve the problem, and then ask students to explain how they solved the problem. Providing a forum for a number of different solutions to be presented and defended by students results in rich dialogue. There is a very high level of mental activity associated with social interactions of this nature. Students who are afforded opportunities to take part in these mathematical conversations on a regular basis learn more effectively how to reason and defend their answers. In the process, they also learn to communicate and to clarify and refine their ideas, which leads to deeper understanding.

When students are able to communicate their ideas, the teacher is provided with insight into their thinking. As an example, the following problem might be given to students.

> **A minivan can seat 6 students plus the driver.** *How many minivans will be needed to transport a class of 32 students on a field trip?*

Students will solve this problem in a variety of ways.
- They might draw rectangles to represent buses and put 6 tally marks in each rectangle to stand for the number of students each van will hold.
- Some might count by sixes.
- Students might apply the division algorithm to this problem—getting an answer of 5 remainder 2.

This last solution prompts an interesting discussion. *What does a remainder of 2 really mean in this problem? Can you have 2 students left over? Does a remainder make sense in this situation?* Going back to the question of how many minivans will be needed all together helps clarify the answer. Because the students have had additional time to review and reflect on the problem, their understanding is enhanced.

Putting ideas on paper is another means of helping students organize their thinking. Writing causes a student to reflect on ideas and refine them before committing that thinking to paper. Often, at the end of a lesson, students will be asked to communicate what they learned in the problem or investigation they just completed. This reflection can be an important tool for teachers in assessing their students' understanding. Words, pictures, numbers and symbols are all important parts of written communication that students have at their disposal, and students are becoming much more adept at using mathematical symbols to communicate their thinking. Many teachers use journal writing as a way for students to relate what they know about mathematics.

Intermediate students should be provided with regular opportunities to use both oral and written language and to share mathematical ideas with their teachers and peers on a daily basis.

Intermediate Connections

MAKING CONNECTIONS IN MATHEMATICS is a three-fold process. First, connections are made when one mathematical idea is used to build another. Second, connections are made among different mathematical ideas. Third, connections are made between mathematics and contexts outside the field of mathematics.

Because mathematics is an integrated discipline, treating it as a whole body of knowledge and focusing on the connections that occur naturally adds dimension to ideas and concepts. How is counting related to addition, addition to subtraction, addition to multiplication, multiplication to area? A cohesive curriculum that is clearly articulated from pre-kindergarten through the twelfth grade, one that connects the mathematical ideas within each grade as well as the mathematics between grade levels, is critical if those connections are to take place.

Making connections to prior mathematical experiences is vital for the understanding of how mathematical ideas build on one another. Teachers need to know what mathematics students learned previously in order to build on that knowledge. In a given unit of study, attention should be paid to ensure that mathematics concepts build upon one another from day to day in a coherent manner. Teachers should also be aware of what their students will be studying in subsequent grades so they can lay the foundation for obvious connections to further studies.

Mathematics permeates other subject areas as well as the physical world of students. The use of shapes and patterns is prevalent in art and architecture; measurement skills and classification skills are important in science; measurement skills and knowledge of fractions are utilized in cooking and building models; and measurement skills and data gathering and statistics are applied in the social sciences.

In grades 3–5, students will be building on the foundation laid in the primary grades. They will be taking their knowledge of addition and subtraction and connecting it to the study of multiplication and division. They will connect

division to the study of fractions. They will take what they have learned about identifying, building, and extending patterns to making predictions about patterns. Measurement in primary grades focused on nonstandard measures. Students will transfer that knowledge to working with standard measures. They will increase the sophistication of the study of data, probability, and statistics. Many of the concrete representations used in the primary grades will evolve to symbolic forms.

There are countless ways to make connections with the mathematics studied in these grades. For example, students enjoy taking surveys of their peers' preferences in food, music, movies, and games. This can be connected to collecting, organizing, and displaying the data in a way that makes sense — important skills that help students to better understand and interpret information presented in the world around them. Analyzing the data gathered from these surveys can be connected to interesting statistical problems. The teacher might pose the questions or have students generate their own.

Calculating the cost of having a class party that includes refreshments, prizes for games, and paper products is a relevant problem for intermediate age students. An activity of this type makes connections to a real world problem. Working in teams, students can estimate how much to order as they generate a menu and supplies that will be needed, and they can calculate costs to work within a given budget. This kind of problem also encourages them to do cost comparisons among various brands.

It is important for teachers to be conscious of connections that can be made in mathematics and to weave those connections into daily practice. When students are able to connect mathematical ideas both inside and outside of the classroom, they begin to see mathematics as a cohesive body of knowledge.

Intermediate Representation

REPRESENTATIONS PROVIDE VEHICLES for expressing and internalizing mathematical thought. They are a critical component in shaping the way students access, understand, express, and utilize mathematical ideas. Representations include physical objects, pictures, and symbols. They also include mental images, words, and ideas.

Representations can be formal or informal. Examples of formal representations are the conventional symbols, graphs, and diagrams traditionally introduced in school mathematics. Informal representations are often invented by students as a way of making sense of mathematical ideas and communicating those ideas to classmates or the teacher. Students should be allowed to create their own understanding and explanations to express relationships before more conventional representations are introduced. Connecting to their invented forms will facilitate a meaningful transition to thinking and communicating in the language of mathematics.

As teachers design lessons, choosing the representations they feel will best help students understand a concept becomes an important consideration. What shared mathematical language is needed to effectively communicate ideas? What manipulatives or models will be appropriate? How will students record their understanding of the concept? When is it appropriate to move from physical to symbolic representations?

In the intermediate grades students begin learning about multiplication conceptually, with concrete objects, often in groups or sets.

> *If there are 3 sets of marbles and there are 3 marbles in each set,*
> *how many marbles are there all together?*

Students will use the marbles from the marble jar to make three groups and count the groups to discover there are 9. Students also learn they can represent that concept by drawing pictures of 3 marbles in three different groups. They extend that knowledge to represent the concept as repeated addition, writing $3 + 3 + 3 = 9$. In grades 3–5 students learn to represent the same situation as multiplication and write $3 \times 3 = 9$. This abstract equation makes sense to them because they have seen the connections through various representative models.

Intermediate grade students still continue to use non-conventional methods to help them interpret new concepts. For example, the teacher may pose the following problem.

Which is more, $\frac{1}{4}$ of a set of 16 items or $\frac{1}{3}$ of a set of 15 items?

Most students at this level do not yet have the means to approach this problem symbolically. Some students will use physical models, such as centimeter cubes to help them determine the answer. Many will make a drawing and will use various representations.

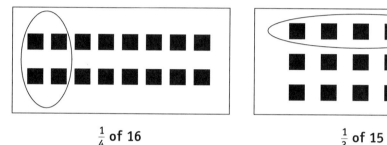

$\frac{1}{4}$ **of 16** $\quad\quad\quad\quad\quad\quad\quad\quad$ $\frac{1}{3}$ **of 15**

Students will be able to conclude that $\frac{1}{3}$ of 15 is a greater amount than $\frac{1}{4}$ of 16. This form of representation allows students to understand a process. It also provides an opportunity for the teacher to connect the visual representation with the equations $\frac{1}{3} \times 15 = 5$ and $\frac{1}{4} \times 16 = 4$ as another way of describing the results.

There are multiple representations for any mathematics concept. The greater the number of ways to represent the same idea, the greater the flexibility available in solving problems. For example, the number 25 can be thought of as 2 tens and 5 ones; as a quarter; as halfway between 1 and 50; as the square of 5; as an odd number; as one more than 24; as five less than 30; as 12 + 13; and so on. A student with access to this variety of representations of 25 is able to choose which version is useful for a particular situation.

One successful way to build multiple representations is to designate a number of the week and encourage students to build a repertoire of ways to represent that number. You might begin with a number such as 27, and ask students to find as many ways as they can to represent that number in 3 minutes. Record their findings on chart paper and post them for students to reflect upon. Revisit the problem for approximately 3 minutes each day. Encourage creative thinking by asking probing questions. *Is there a way to make 27 using multiplication AND division? Can 27 be made using three operations?* By the end of the week, you will have a chart full of interesting representations. If students engage in this type of activity on a regular basis, they will become fluid in their thinking about numbers.

20 + 7 = 27   9 + 18 = 27   (4 x 6) + 3 = 27
12 + 15 = 27   3 x 9 = 27   30 – 3 = 27
(5 x 5) + 2 = 27   (28 ÷ 4) + (2 x 10) = 27

Conclusion

The process standards are not an end, in and of themselves. Rather, they provide the advanced organizers or plan for lessons that present important mathematics content. Seeing connections among mathematical topics enables students to reason and make sense of new ideas and problem-solving situations they encounter. Through the process of communication, students are able to represent these new ideas either formally or informally.

Just as the process standards are interrelated, so are the process and content standards. For true mathematical thinking and learning to occur, both process and content need to be skillfully woven into and through each lesson. That is the goal to work toward.

Standard 1 **Number and Operation**

AT THE THIRD GRADE LEVEL, number and operation include work with all four of the basic operations, developing mental math strategies and ability, and building fractional concepts. Our lessons are derived from these important topics. They include a lesson on using patterns to build mental math ability, a lesson that develops understanding of multiplication, a lesson that explores division concepts, and a lesson that develops fractional concepts.

Three lessons model how the process standards can be used to teach content. A fourth lesson is a hypothetical textbook lesson that we have revised to be more standards based. These four lessons do not represent the entire curriculum, but rather provide glimpses of how, with a more concentrated effort to incorporate the process standards, better mathematics teaching and learning can be achieved.

One lesson we have chosen uses patterns on a hundred chart to develop mental math strategies for addition. Students make connections between their knowledge of the basic facts and patterns on the hundred chart to build mental math strategies. By discussing ideas with classmates, students are able to learn or refine new strategies.

Another lesson we have chosen develops the concept of multiplication. Students create visual representations of rectangular arrays. They use the arrays to make connections to area, repeated addition, and multiplication. Students discuss how repeated addition leads to multiplication.

A third lesson we have chosen focuses on the concept of division. Students use a problem-solving approach to realize that whether a situation requires finding the number of groups or the number of objects in each group, division is required. Students use communication and reasoning to discuss methods for solving the problems.

The hypothetical textbook lesson we have chosen to revise is one that focuses on understanding fractions as parts of a whole. Students make connections to their prior experiences with fractions, and discuss the terms part and whole as they relate to these situations. Students make representations of fraction situations by paper folding and creating drawings. They use these representations to make connections to the symbolic form for expressing fractions.

Standard 1 Lessons

**Applying Patterns
to Mental Math**

Understanding Multiplication

Investigating Division

**Understanding Fractions
as Parts of Wholes**

Applying Patterns to Mental Math

Introduction

Objective → Students will use patterns in the hundred chart to develop mental math strategies for addition.

Context → Students know basic facts in addition and subtraction and have learned the algorithm for two-digit numbers without regrouping. They will move on to learning the standard algorithm for addition with regrouping.

NCTM Standards Focus

Students are often taught to add symbolically without looking at patterns. In this lesson, students use the hundred chart as a visual tool to recognize and learn patterns. When they have explored patterns on the hundred chart, they then connect these patterns to mental math strategies and to symbolic notation. By incorporating the following three process standards, students learn patterns and strategies they can use to solve other problems.

Representation Students use a hundred chart to recognize and learn patterns for adding using mental math.

Connections Students connect their prior knowledge of basic facts in addition to patterns on the hundred chart in order to develop mental math strategies.

Communication Students communicate to their classmates the strategies and solutions they developed using the hundred chart and they explain how these helped them to add mentally. They learn about the strategies and patterns their classmates developed and use what they learned to evaluate and refine their own strategies.

Teaching Plan

Materials → Student pages 22–23

ATTACH A LARGE HUNDRED CHART to the wall or the board. Ask students to describe the number patterns they see in the chart. Students should notice that moving from left to right in any row shows a counting up, or + 1, pattern and that moving down a row in a column shows a + 10 pattern.

Refresh students' memory on how to add 10, 20, or 30 to any number by playing a few rounds of "What's My Rule?" Have one student pick a number on the hundred chart. Another student adds 10, 20, or 30 to that number. A third student tells what the rule is, and a fourth student tells which number would come next if you moved one space to the right from the original number and then applied the rule.

Once students are comfortable adding multiples of 10 to a number, place students in groups of 2 to 4 and give them the hundred chart on student page 22. Have them discuss and write the answers to the questions at the bottom of the page. Then write the following set of examples on the board or overhead.

34 and 9 is _____   63 and 9 is _____

87 and 9 is _____   49 and 9 is _____

HAVE STUDENTS WORK in their assigned groups to find the solutions. Tell them to keep a record of what they do and discuss so they can use it when they communicate their strategies and solutions to the class. When all groups have finished each example, have a volunteer from each group share his/her group's methods and strategies.

Methods Students Might Use
- Begin with the first number and count on 9 squares by 1s.
- Move down 1 square to add 10. Then move left 1 square to subtract 1 from 10.

ENCOURAGE STUDENTS TO SEE that one way to show a pattern is to write a number sentence, or use numerical notation. *How can you represent moving down 1 square using numbers and symbols?* (+ 10) *How would you show moving down 1 square and 1 square to the left using numerical notation?* (+ 10 − 1).

What Might Happen . . . What to Do

Some students might be insecure about mentally adding numbers other than 10 because they are comfortable with counting. Ask the students who added 9 by counting on by 1s to add 10 to a number. Have them check their answers on the hundred chart. *What do you notice about the placement of the two addends?*

Then discuss the relationship between 10 and 9. *What is their relationship on the hundred chart?* Have students use the chart to add 9 to several different numbers and ask them to communicate each move before they make it. Encourage them to use the words "add" and "subtract" with each move.

---

f.y.i.

You might suggest that students use two rulers, pencils, or slips of paper to help keep track of where they are in each row and column.

GIVE STUDENTS SOME ADDITIONAL PROBLEMS that involve adding 9 to a number. Encourage them to answer the questions orally, using the symbolic pattern + 10 − 1 without looking at the hundred chart. This encourages students to practice using mental math to add 9 to any number. Ask them to explain how using the pattern + 10 − 1 makes adding 9 to a number easier than other strategies they might have used before.

Give students the following problems:

27 and 19 is _____   76 and 19 is _____

59 + 19 = _____   84 + 19 = _____

Have them use the hundred chart to find the solutions. *What did you do to find the answer?* Observe and listen to how students approach and solve the problem. Are they making connections to the similarities between adding 19 and adding 9? Students should realize that to add 19 using the chart, they move 2 squares down and 1 square to the left. Are students representing their work on the hundred chart symbolically as + 20 − 1?

CONTINUE THE LESSON by presenting problems that add 29 to any number from 1 to 69. This time the students should see that the pattern is to add 30, then subtract 1. Give the problems orally and have students respond by using either the hundred chart or mental math.

Extensions

Whenever time allows, have students use the hundred chart to add 8, 18, and 28. Students should realize that they need to move down 1, 2, or 3 squares, then left 2 squares. Encourage them to develop the mental math strategy of adding 10, 20, or 30, and subtracting 2.

As a further extension, you might want students to use the hundred chart to subtract 9, 19, and 29. The movement is now up 1, 2, or 3 squares and over 1 square to the right.

Student Pages

Student page 22 contains the hundred chart that students use during the lesson and some questions to answer regarding the chart. Student page 23 contains practice addition problems for which students can use the hundred chart or the mental math strategies they developed during the lesson. This page also asks students to explain the patterns they used to solve the problems.

Assessment

As students worked together to solve addition problems, you were able to observe how well they began to internalize the use of patterns to develop mental math strategies. Class discussions in which students explained how they used the hundred charts to recognize patterns and develop mental math strategies gave you additional opportunities for assessing students' progress. The practice problems on student page 23 can also help you assess an individual student's progress.

NCTM Standards Summary

Students used the hundred chart as a visual representation that helped them recognize patterns and then use those patterns to develop mental math strategies for adding numbers close to multiples of 10. Students connected the patterns they observed on the hundred chart to mathematical operations. They communicated their recognition of patterns and the strategies they applied during the lesson to their classmates. They listened to the methods developed by other students and adjusted their own thinking accordingly.

Answers

Page 22
1. The numbers are always $+1$.
2. When you move down a column, the numbers are $+10$; to the right is $+11$; and to the left is $+9$.
3. When you move up a column, the numbers are -10; to the right is -9; and to the left is -11.

Page 23
Patterns used by students to solve the problems will vary.
1. 16
2. 26
3. 36
4. 37
5. 47
6. 57
7. 85
8. 75
9. 65
10. 94
11. 84
12. 74

Applying Patterns to Mental Math

Use the hundred chart to answer the questions.

1	2	3	4	5	6	7	8	9	10
11	12	13	14	15	16	17	18	19	20
21	22	23	24	25	26	27	28	29	30
31	32	33	34	35	36	37	38	39	40
41	42	43	44	45	46	47	48	49	50
51	52	53	54	55	56	57	58	59	60
61	62	63	64	65	66	67	68	69	70
71	72	73	74	75	76	77	78	79	80
81	82	83	84	85	86	87	88	89	90
91	92	93	94	95	96	97	98	99	100

❶ What happens when you move across a row in the hundred chart?

❷ What happens when you move down a column and then move to the right? When you move down and to the left?

❸ What happens when you move up a column and then move to the right? When you move down and to the left?

Standard 1 Number and Operation

Applying Patterns to Mental Math

Use the hundred chart or mental math to solve each problem.
Under each problem, write the pattern you used to solve the problem.

1 7 + 9 =

2 7 + 19 =

3 7 + 29 =

4 8 + 29 =

5 18 + 29 =

6 28 + 29 =

7 56 + 29 =

8 56 + 19 =

9 56 + 9 =

10 65 + 29 =

11 65 + 19 =

12 65 + 9 =

13 Write a problem using a new pattern. Tell how you thought of your pattern. Tell why it makes solving your problem easier.

Understanding Multiplication

Introduction

Objective → Students will understand the concept of multiplication through repeated addition and arrays.

Context → Students have begun learning the multiplication facts by the use of addition and function tables. They will work toward mastery of the multiplication facts.

NCTM Standards Focus

By creating and using a model, students can see or visualize what repeated addition and multiplication actually look like. In most presentations, students operate mainly on symbols or sets. When working with whole numbers, the quantity becomes larger but doesn't have the same visual impact as an array. In this standards-based lesson, students will see a one-to-one correspondence between the numbers in a multiplication sentence and the length and width of the array or rectangle.

Representation Students use rectangles to represent the idea of multiplication or repeated addition. They draw rectangles on grid paper to create a visual representation of area, repeated addition, and multiplication. By using grid paper, students can show a one-to-one correspondence between the numbers in a given multiplication sentence and the length and width of the rectangle or array that represents that sentence.

Connections Students make connections between the model of an array, repeated addition, and multiplication. They also make connections with geometry and measurement since they are finding the area of a rectangular array.

Communication Students share what they find out about multiplication and repeated addition. They discuss their findings, listen to their classmates, and ask questions about methods or ideas. They keep records of their group findings and discussions.

Teaching Plan

Materials → Student pages 28–29

Have students work individually or in pairs to draw and study pictures that represent multiplication problems. Give students grid paper (student page 28). Ask them to draw a line 8 squares long across the paper. From the beginning of the horizontal line, have them draw a line down that is 5 squares long. Have them enclose the rectangle and then figure out how many squares are inside the rectangle. Explain that as they do this, they will be finding the area of the rectangle. Encourage them to write down exactly how they arrive at the area, using words, numbers, and number sentences as well as their thoughts on the activity. They will have a chance to share their thinking and their strategies with the rest of the class.

As students tackle the problem, observe the methods they use. Ask them to tell how they are approaching the problem by asking questions like: *What have you already done? What will you do next? Why?* Encourage students to show how they used the rectangle on the grid for their solutions. When students come back together, have them share their results. Here are some things you should see. If you do not see any of these strategies or methods, you might want to model some or all of them.

Methods Students Might Use

- They counted the squares by 1s.
- They separated rows of 8, counted the squares in each row, and added those figures.
- They wrote the addition sentence $8 + 8 + 8 + 8 + 8 = 40$.
- They separated, counted, and added the columns.
- They wrote the addition sentence $5 + 5 + 5 + 5 + 5 + 5 + 5 + 5 = 40$.
- They skip-counted by 5s.
- They skip-counted by 8s.
- They used the multiplication sentence $5 \times 8 = 40$.

```
□ □ □ □ □ □ □    8
□ □ □ □ □ □ □    8    5 × 8 = 40
□ □ □ □ □ □ □    8
□ □ □ □ □ □ □    8    8 + 8 + 8 + 8 + 8 = 40
□ □ □ □ □ □ □    8
5  5  5  5  5  5  5  5 | 40
           8 × 5 = 40
           5 + 5 + 5 + 5 + 5 + 5 + 5 + 5 = 40
```

MODEL STUDENTS' THOUGHTS about counting and adding as addition sentences if they have not mentioned the repeated addition sentences or the multiplication sentences during the discussion. Skip-counting lends itself to representing the multiplication sentences. Ask students to tell how the rectangle represents 5×8 and 8×5. As they explain how you can look at the rectangle either horizontally or vertically, help them to notice that the position of the factors does not change the product.

f.y.i.

Sometimes well-known songs and stories can serve as a springboard to explorations. The song "Inchworm" is fairly well known and lends itself to talking about multiplication. The doubling exercises also show a different way to multiply. Have children draw enclosed rectangles for each doubling exercise and write the accompanying number sentences.

Help students make the connection that the commutative property in addition also works in multiplication. Does this always work in multiplication or does it work only because the representation is a rectangle? Some students might be able to do some simple multiplication facts mentally and conclude that the position of the factors does not matter. If students are not able to answer the question with certainty, return to this idea several times during the lesson. Once students internalize the commutative property of multiplication, they will realize that they already know a lot of multiplication facts and need to memorize only the new facts.

CONTINUE THE DISCUSSION by asking students which method for finding the area of the rectangle was the easiest and the fastest. *How would you change the methods you used? Why? How did representing repeated addition or multiplication by a rectangle make it easier to solve the problem? When can you use multiplication or addition to show the same thing?*

Students should be able to discern that multiplication and addition can be interchanged only if all the addends or groups are of equal size. Representing repeated addition and multiplication as a rectangle gives them a visual image they can always recreate. They should also conclude that since all groups are equal, the representation will always be a rectangle.

Have students enclose additional rectangles and find the areas. Encourage them to write about how they solved each problem and to write repeated addition sentences as well as multiplication sentences for each rectangle. At the end of the lesson, have students discuss the methods they used to solve the problems and how the representations helped them. Three possible grids to use as problems follow.

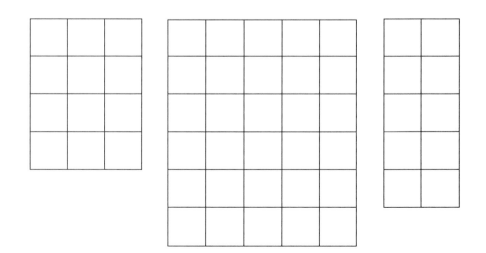

```
┌─────────────────────────────────────────────────────────────────┐
│ What Might Happen . . . What to Do                                │
│ ----------------------------------------------------------------- │
│                                                                   │
│ Some students might draw the        of the rectangles. Skip-counting │
│ rectangles correctly, but will      by 2s, 5s, and 10s is rote for most │
│ continue to count the squares       children. They can also double │
│ by ones. Work with these            almost all one-digit numbers. │
│ students to move gradually to       Connect the skip-counting and │
│ skip-counting, doubling, and/or     doubling to the symbolism of  │
│ adding the rows or columns          number sentences.             │
└─────────────────────────────────────────────────────────────────┘
```

Student Pages

Student page 28 contains a grid on which students can enclose rectangles for the activity. Student page 29 contains additional practice exercises.

Assessment

Observing the students as they were developing the concept of multiplication, you had an opportunity to determine whether they connected the arrays and repeated addition as two ways to express the same thing. You also saw how some students connected repeated addition to multiplication sentences. You could determine whether most of the students moved from counting by 1s to a more sophisticated approach of skip-counting or adding. In addition, you could note how students concluded that the positions of the factors made no difference in the product.

NCTM Standards Summary

Students created a visual image to represent repeated addition and multiplication. They analyzed an array and determined that the order in which the factors were multiplied made no difference to the answer. They connected these ideas to the commutative property in addition. Since the arrays were represented as rectangles, they connected this activity to geometry and measurement of area as well. Students shared what they found out about multiplication and repeated addition. They discussed and listened to the findings of others and adapted their own methods when it made sense to do so.

Answers

Page 29

1. $4 + 4 + 4 + 4 + 4 = 20$
   $5 + 5 + 5 + 5 = 20$, or
   $5 \times 4 = 20$, or $4 \times 5 = 20$
2. $2 + 2 + 2 + 2 + 2 + 2 = 12$
   $6 + 6 = 12$, or
   $6 \times 2 = 12$, or $2 \times 6 = 12$
3. $2 + 2 + 2 = 6$, or $3 + 3 = 6$
   $3 \times 2 = 6$, or $2 \times 3 = 6$
4. $4 + 4 + 4 + 4 = 16$
   $4 \times 4 = 16$
5. $3 + 3 + 3 + 3 + 3 + 3 = 18$,
   or $6 + 6 + 6 = 18$
   $6 \times 3 = 18$, or $3 \times 6 = 18$
6. $4 + 4 + 4 + 4 + 4 + 4 + 4 = 28$,
   or $7 + 7 + 7 + 7 = 28$
   $7 \times 4 = 28$, or $4 \times 7 = 28$

Understanding Multiplication

Use the grid paper for multiplication.

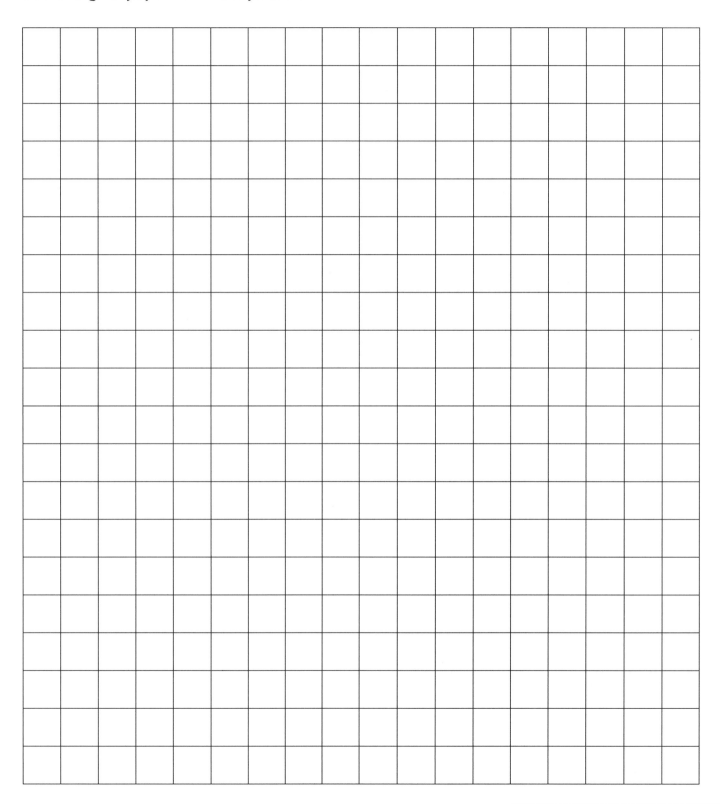

Understanding Multiplication

Write a repeated addition sentence and a multiplication sentence for each rectangle.

❶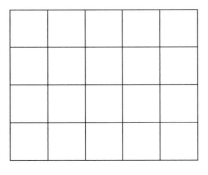

❷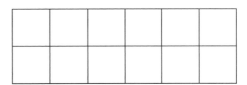

❸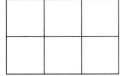

❹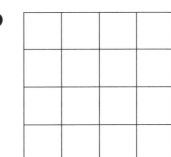

❺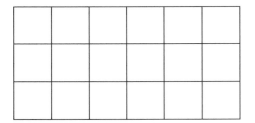

❻

Investigating Division

Introduction

Objective → Students will explore division concepts and devise strategies for solving division problems without concerning themselves with which of the two types of division problems (grouping or measurement and fair share or partitioning) they are solving.

Context → Students are familiar with multiplication facts. They will apply their exploration of division concepts to the formal division algorithm.

NCTM Standards Focus

In this lesson, students explore the two division concepts of grouping and fair share, or sharing. They see that the two kinds of division problems are solved using similar processes and eventually the same algorithm. Since students are allowed to freely explore the two distinct division situations, they can compare and contrast them, which students do not often get the chance to do. Usually, when the division algorithm is introduced, only the sharing concept is presented. By using problem solving and the other two process standards listed here, students learn the differences and similarities in the two division concepts. This will help them recognize that one operation—and one algorithm—can solve many different problems.

Problem Solving Students make sense of given problem-solving situations and determine that they must divide in order to solve the problem. Although they do not need to distinguish between the two types of division problems, they need to recognize that division is applied in both types of situations.

Communication Students analyze the problems to determine strategies that work and discuss the operations that will help them solve the problems. They keep careful records, writing about the steps they take in the solution process as well as any discoveries or generalizations they make.

Reasoning and Proof Students make generalizations about the steps they go through when they deal with the two division concepts. They show that although there are major differences between knowing the number of groups and knowing the number of objects in each set or group, the division steps remain the same. Students share the strategies they develop and show that these strategies work, at least in the problems they are dealing with in this lesson.

Teaching Plan

Materials → Student pages 34–35; money

ARRANGE STUDENTS IN GROUPS and give them student page 34. Have them read the two problems and then work together to decide how to solve them. Remind students to keep notes on their group discussions, methods, and solution processes so they can share their discoveries with the rest of the class. As you observe the groups, listen to their discussions but refrain from asking questions or correcting students—even if some of the methods seem too labor-intensive or incorrect. Return to your observations through questioning during the class discussion.

After the groups have arrived at their solutions, have them share their strategies and methods as well as their thoughts and discussions. Encourage students to question the different approaches.

Methods Students Might Use

- Using paper money, they shared the six 10s and two 1s into five groups (each student is a group). They placed one 10 in each group and changed the leftover 10 to 1s. They kept exchanging the leftover money into coins and physically distributed the smaller and smaller denominations into the five groups until they shared all the money equally. Each student got $12.40. Students' reasoning for solving the problem physically by using money is that they know how many groups they have and they want each group to get an equal amount.

- Students represented the pencils with 62 tally marks and circled each group of 5. They skip-counted by 5s to 60. They could not complete the last group because there were only 2 pencils left. They created groups of 5 because they knew the total number of pencils and the number of pencils placed on each desk, but they didn't know how many desks would get pencils.

- Students drew or used objects to represent the sharing of the money and used subtraction to solve the problem with the pencils. Their reasoning is that they can repeatedly subtract 5 pencils from 62 pencils, but they cannot subtract 5 students from $62.

- Students used the multiplication facts they know and began to solve the first problem symbolically. They continued the solution process by drawing a picture of $2 as coins and distributing the coins equally into 5 groups. They used the same division solution with the second problem, but did not include the remainder of 2, because each group has to have 5 pencils.

- Students used mental math to solve the second problem. They multiplied 5 by 10 and got 50. They showed the subtraction, $62 - 50 = 12$. They continued symbolically: $5 \times 2 = 10$, $12 - 10 = 2$. The remaining 2 pencils were not enough to make 1 more group. Students found the number of times 5 was used as a factor and got 12. They decided to solve the

f.y.i.

Since the students will work in groups, you might want to introduce the two types of division problems to the class as a warm-up. If there are 24 students in your class, tell them that you want to form 8 groups (adjust the numbers as needed), and ask how many would be in each group. Then tell students that you have changed your mind and have them figure out how many groups there would be if each group has 4 members. Talk about how they figured out the two answers and how the problems are different.

problem mentally because they found the multiplication and subtraction simple to do.

What Might Happen . . . What to Do

If some students do not see that both problems deal with division, refer them back to the warm-up problems. Have them explain the steps they took as they worked the problems, and their answers. Encourage them to show the activity symbolically using a division sentence, subtraction, or skip-counting. Then have them explain how the grouping problem is different from the sharing problem. Encourage as much detail as possible.

PROBE THE STUDENTS WITH QUESTIONS about how the first two division problems—sharing and grouping—are the same and different. Assess students' understanding of the fact that although the two problems have the same numbers—62, 5, and an unknown—the problem situations are different. Without naming the two different division concepts, here are some of the main ideas students should note:

- The numbers in both problems are the same.
- In the grouping problem, students know how many are in each group and need to find how many groups there are in all. In the sharing problem, they know how many groups there are and need to find how many in each group.
- In the grouping problem, they can separate the number in a group from the total number by subtracting. In the sharing problem, they cannot subtract because the whole and the part are different.
- In the grouping problem, they can skip-count by the number that is in the group. In the sharing problem, they can use multiplication.
- In the grouping problem, they can draw pictures of the groups until they reach the number of the whole. In the sharing problem, they can draw a picture of the whole and partition it into groups.

If time permits, give students the third division problem on student page 34 and have them solve the problem individually. Have students record the steps they took to solve it. When they have finished, have them write a word problem that fits their solution process. As you observe them, ask if the divisor 8 stands for the number of groups or the number of objects in each group.

This lesson focuses on students' understanding that there are two distinct division concepts. Students do not need to name the concepts as sharing and grouping, but rather to explain how the concepts are similar and how they differ. Since students can only differentiate between the two concepts by the processes they adopt, group and class communications play a vital role in this lesson. Although the formal division algorithm is not presented here, the lesson is a precursor to the formal algorithm and includes all of its steps.

Student Pages

Student page 34 contains the problems used during the lesson and a problem for students to work on individually. Student page 35 has practice and application problems for students to solve and complete.

Assessment

As you observed students working in groups, you saw how they processed the problems and communicated their understanding of the different operations to each other. The group and class discussions gave you an opportunity to assess students' understanding of the two different division concepts. Then as students individually solved the division sentence and formulated a word problem, you had an opportunity to assess how well they distinguished between the two division concepts.

NCTM Standards Summary

Using problem solving, students analyzed and made sense of the two types of division concepts. They explained how the two concepts are similar and how they differ. They recorded the processes they employed and shared their conclusions using communication. They used reasoning and proof to make generalizations and to conclude that even though there were major differences between knowing the number of groups and knowing the number of objects in each group, the operation of division remained the same.

Answers

Page 34

1. $12.40

2. 12 desks

3. 7 for a grouping problem; $7\frac{1}{2}$ for a sharing problem dealing with something that can be divided into parts; 7 for a sharing problem dealing with something that cannot be divided.

Page 35

1. 14 remainder 1 or $14\frac{1}{4}$

2. 11 remainder 3 or $11\frac{1}{2}$

3. 11 remainder 6 or $11\frac{6}{7}$

4. 25

5. $22.50

6. 12 tables

7. 13 cubes

8. 12 crayons

9. 13 full weeks

10. 18 raisins

Investigating Division

Solve the problems.

1 After a snowstorm, 5 students shoveled sidewalks and driveways. They earned $62. If they share the money equally, how much will each student get?

2 The classroom helper has 62 pencils and is placing 5 pencils on each desk in the class. On how many desks can the helper place 5 pencils?

3 Solve the division sentence. Write about the steps you needed to solve it. Then write a word problem that fits your solution.

$60 \div 8 =$ _____

Investigating Division

Solve the problems. Write a word problem for each.

❶ 57 ÷ 4 = _____

❷ 69 ÷ 6 = _____

❸ 83 ÷ 7 = _____

❹ 75 ÷ 3 = _____

Solve the word problems. Write how they are the same and different.

❺ Suni and 3 friends made $90 in profits selling lemonade. How much profit does each one get?

❻ There are 96 people at the soccer dinner. Each table can seat 8 people. How many tables are needed?

❼ Lena cut out 82 squares to make cubes with 6 faces. How many cubes can she make?

❽ After the art class, Anansa helps put 72 crayons into 6 boxes. Each box has the same number of crayons. How many crayons are in each box?

❾ Jaycee's class figured out that there are 68 days left in the school year. How many full school weeks is that, if each school week has 5 days?

❿ Tia, Kimu, Jamal, and Jessica shared a small box of 72 raisins. How many raisins did each of them get?

Understanding Fractions as Parts of Wholes

Introduction

Objective → Students will understand fractions as equal parts of a whole.

Context → This fraction lesson occurs early in the unit. Students have had recent experiences folding paper into equal-sized sections and have been introduced to the terms *whole* and *part*. In subsequent lessons, students will learn that fractions can also represent parts of larger sets, and they will be introduced to mixed numbers.

Understanding Fractions as Parts of Wholes

Learn

A fraction names a part of a whole.

The rectangle is divided into 4 equal parts.

One part of the rectangle is shaded.

$\frac{1}{4}$ of the rectangle is shaded.

$\frac{1}{4}$ 1 Numerator—the part that is shaded
     4 Denominator—the number of equal parts

Take a look at these other fractions.

$\frac{3}{4}$
3 out of 4 are shaded. Three fourths are shaded.

$\frac{4}{6}$
4 out of 6 are shaded. Four sixths are shaded.

$\frac{5}{8}$
5 out of 8 are shaded. Five eighths are shaded.

Explore

Why can we say "1 divided by four" instead of $\frac{1}{4}$? _____

_____

_____

NCTM Process Standards Analysis and Focus

The standards analysis examines how the process standards have been incorporated into the above lesson. By increasing the focus on three of the process standards, a more effective and meaningful lesson can be presented. The suggestions offered can help you to think about how this might be accomplished.

Connections Geometric figures on the text pages connect area models with the concept of fractions.

Suggestion → Draw on students' experiences with fractions as equal parts of a whole by using familiar situations in which fractions are used. Making such connections will help students understand the important role fractions play in daily life. Help students connect

Practice

What is the part that is shaded? Express your answers in words and numbers.

1.

2.

3.

4.

5.

6.

Draw and shade these fractions.

7. $\frac{3}{4}$

8. $\frac{2}{3}$

9. $\frac{1}{6}$

10. $\frac{3}{5}$

11. $\frac{1}{4}$

12. $\frac{3}{8}$

13. four ninths

14. five out of seven

15. three tenths

16. one divided by three

17. five divided by six

18. three out of thirteen

Problem Solving

19. Terry ordered a pizza. She ate $\frac{1}{4}$ of it. Draw the pizza and shade what was left.

20. Shawn made a square game board. He colored $\frac{3}{8}$ of the board. Draw what the board might look like.

physical representations of fractions with the symbols used to describe them by having students label models.

Representation The lesson uses only drawings of geometric figures to represent fractions. This limits students' ability to develop a rich understanding of the concept presented.

Suggestion → Have students create drawings and use paper folding to represent fractions that directly relate to familiar situations in their daily lives. Asking students to label fractional parts with appropriate numerical symbols will help them recognize different representations of the same amount.

Communication The lesson presents limited opportunities for students to exchange ideas.

Suggestion → Encourage students to communicate their ideas about fair shares and equal parts using the terms *part* and *whole*. As students identify fractions, have them explain their use of terms and symbols.

Problem Solving Problem solving is limited since students can simply follow directions to shade portions of the figures shown.

Reasoning and Proof The critical thinking question "Why can you describe $\frac{1}{4}$ as 1 divided by 4?" requires high level reasoning and, at this point in the curriculum, may be too difficult for students to comprehend.

The teaching plan that follows shows how the suggestions for increasing the focus on the process standards can be implemented.

Revised Teaching Plan

BEGIN BY ASKING STUDENTS TO DRAW PICTURES of real-life examples of fractions. *Draw a picture of a glass of milk that's half gone. Draw a big sandwich and show how you would share it equally with three friends. If you had to share a pizza fairly with everyone in your family, how would you slice it?* These drawings help students to start thinking of fractions as equal parts of wholes. Ask students to think of additional fraction situations: *Are there other times you have to divide things up into equal parts? Can you describe some of these times for us?*

Students have an understanding of dividing a whole into equal parts through their experiences of sharing. Representing fractions with real-life situations at the start of the lesson builds connections to familiar contexts and promotes clarity as students use those understandings to create drawings of fractions.

What Might Happen . . . What to Do

A common misconception in drawing fractions involves dividing something into parts without considering equality. For example, a student might divide a whole into three unequal parts, as shown, but identify each portion of the figure as one third.

Reinforce the connections between equal parts and students' prior knowledge by having students recall the discussion about sharing a sandwich or a pizza. Emphasize the idea that fractions are fair shares.

Check to see that students are creating wholes divided into equal parts as they work on their drawings.

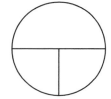

DEMONSTRATE HOW TO LABEL EACH PART of a fractional drawing with the appropriate numerical symbol that names the fraction. Model the use of the terms *fraction, part,* and *whole* in describing fraction situations students are familiar with. Remind students that each piece or part is called a *fraction* and that what is being divided is called the *whole. The number on the bottom, called the* denominator, *shows the total number of parts that the whole has been divided into. The number on top is called the* numerator *and it shows the number of parts you have.* A powerful bridge to understanding is built when students can represent a familiar situation with appropriate mathematical language. Work through several examples on the board before asking students to label their drawings.

Circulate and observe as students use numerical symbols to label their fraction drawings. Ask questions to confirm that students are developing understanding. *Why is there a 3 below the line? How many parts are shaded here? How many parts are in this whole?* Insisting on the use of the terms *part* and *whole* will help students develop the vocabulary they need to think about fractions in a meaningful way.

What Might Happen . . . What to Do

Students may have trouble keeping the numerator and denominator straight. You might ask them to think of a familiar situation that they know for a fraction such as $\frac{1}{2}$ of a pizza and make a connection to the numerical representation. *There were two parts in the whole pizza, and so the number 2 goes below the line in the denominator. Now I just have one of the pieces, and so the number 1 goes above the line in the numerator.* Have students visualize the mathematical symbol with the pizza. They can use that visual connection as a reminder to help them when writing other fractions.

f.y.i.

Students may become preoccupied with exact paper folding. The fraction concept is the focus of the lesson, not accurate creasing. Let students know that while it is important that they understand that each part is *supposed to be* exactly the same size, paper folding is not exact and they should not worry about trying to be perfect in their folding.

INSTRUCT STUDENTS TO FOLD PAPER into equal parts as another way to show the fractions they have drawn. Representing the same fraction in different ways increases understanding of that fraction. As an example, have students represent the half-full glass of milk they drew using a sheet of paper folded into two equal parts, with the fold symbolizing the division between the empty top and the full bottom. Students can then label and color the bottom half.

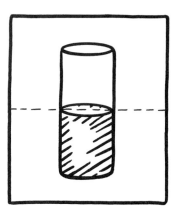

Ask students to fold, shade in, and label several fractions you assign. Mix real-life examples and abstract fractions. *Show me $\frac{3}{4}$ on a whole sheet of paper. Show a board that has had $\frac{1}{6}$ painted.* You may wish to have students work alone and use the activity as an opportunity for assessment, or you may prefer to provide further practice by having students work in pairs or small groups and discuss their approaches to each problem.

Consider having some challenging bonus problems such as fifths and sevenths for early finishers.

END THE LESSON WITH A SIMPLE GAME, "Is This the Right Fraction?" Write a fraction on the board. Then draw either its representation or that of another fraction. Have students vote thumbs up if the picture you drew is correct for the fraction, thumbs down if it is incorrect. Be sure to include at least one example of a drawing that is incorrect because the parts are unequal. Ask students to justify their answers and encourage them to use the new terminology they are learning in their explanations.

Student Pages

Students are now ready to complete practice exercises similar to those shown on the reduced student pages.

Assessment

Drawings and paper-folded models made by students demonstrated their understanding of the concept of fractions as equal parts of a whole. Labeling models and playing "Is This the Right Fraction?" presented opportunities to assess students' understanding of symbolic representation.

NCTM Standards Summary

Having students make connections to prior knowledge by thinking about fractions they use in everyday life added meaning to the concept being developed. As students represented fractions with drawings and paper-folded models, they focused on fractions as equal shares or equal parts of a whole. In labeling their fractions, connections were made between concrete models and abstract representation. Encouraging students to explain the symbols as they labeled fractions reinforced understanding of the connection between the appropriate written form and the fractional model.

Standard 2 **Algebra**

A T T H E T H I R D G R A D E L E V E L , algebra includes a lot of work with multiplication, division, fractions, and problem solving. Our lessons are derived from these important topics. They include a lesson on using patterns to solve problems, a lesson that relates multiplication and division, a lesson that relates fractions and division, and a lesson that establishes the commutative property for multiplication.

Three lessons model how the process standards can be used to teach content. A fourth lesson is a hypothetical textbook lesson that we have revised to be more standards based. These four lessons do not represent the entire curriculum, but rather provide glimpses of how, with a more concentrated effort to incorporate the process standards, better mathematics teaching and learning can be achieved.

One lesson we have chosen uses patterns to solve problems. Students apply their problem-solving strategies to extending patterns and to using patterns to represent algebraic situations.

Another lesson we have chosen relates multiplication and division. Connections are made to students' prior experiences with addition and subtraction, which have a similar relationship. Students write division facts from multiplication sentences, and use this relationship to check their answers to division problems and to find a missing number in a number sentence.

A third lesson we have chosen explores the relationship between fractions and division. Connections and representations are important to this lesson because students link their knowledge of division to fractions of a set. Students use manipulatives to model division and fractions of a set, and write fractional notation to show the fraction of a set.

The hypothetical textbook lesson we have chosen to revise is one that focuses on the commutative property of multiplication. Through better incorporation of the process standards of representation, connections, and reasoning and proof, students will see visually, by rotating rectangular arrays, that the order of the factors does not change the result. Students are also asked to try to find a counter-example that would disprove the commutative property.

Standard 2 Lessons

Using Patterns to
Solve Problems

Relating Multiplication
and Division

Relating Fractions and Division

Exploring Properties
of Multiplication

Using Patterns to Solve Problems

Introduction

Objective → Students will describe, extend, and make generalizations about geometric and numeric sequential patterns.

Context → Throughout the primary grades, children have had experiences building, representing, and describing patterns. They have also identified the repeating unit in patterns. In later lessons, children will continue to identify, describe, and generalize relationships as rules that can be expressed algebraically.

NCTM Standards Focus

In this standards-based lesson, students are presented with problems that involve patterns and can be solved in multiple ways. Students who have had experiences with determining numerical patterns and stating the rule on their own have a better understanding of the concept than whose who have dealt only with obvious geometric patterns where they have simply repeated the pattern. The students' thinking about the problems and the strategies they use in this lesson will enhance their mathematical understanding of patterns and relationships.

Problem Solving Students apply problem-solving strategies that they have learned, especially those involving pattern recognition, or devise their own methods to analyze problems and solve them.

Connections Students extend their understanding of patterns to algebraic situations. They look for and use patterns to solve problems.

Communication Students share strategies and discuss how they think about and approach the problems. Communicating about mathematics provides students an opportunity to review and revise their thinking and to learn about new strategies.

Teaching Plan

Materials → Student pages 48–49; chart paper; pattern blocks

START THIS LESSON with a quick review of patterns. Write the pattern and the sequence on the board:

1	3	1	3	1	3
1	4	7	10	13	16

Have students tell what they know about the pattern and the sequence and ask them to explain how they could extend each for the next three numbers. Have students compare the pattern and the sequence, noting the similarities and differences between them. It is important that students see that both are predictable, but that the first one is a repeating pattern and the second one is a sequence that grows by three. Help students to focus on this difference. *What numbers will you see in the first pattern?* (1 and 3) *What numbers will you see in the second?* (19, 22, 25, 28, . . .) Be sure that students see that numbers are repeated in the first pattern, but not in the second.

Now tell students they will be using what they know about patterns to solve problems. Tell them to imagine that they are selling shapes. The order department at the Shape Company prices orders according to the number of sides purchased. The students' first task is to find a method for telling how many sides customers will get if they order from 1–10 triangles. The method selected should be one that can be used again and again as different orders are placed. Show the students a drawing of a triangle and review quickly the number of sides.

Allow students to work in pairs. Give them sufficient time to devise their systems. While students are working make sure they understand that their goal is to create a system that can be used many times during the day— perhaps even by another person.

AFTER STUDENTS HAVE FINISHED, bring them back together to discuss what they have done. Have students present their systems and invite the class to evaluate the different systems to see how accurate and useful they are. Students will probably come up with a chart or list that represents the number of sides for the different triangles. Methods for finding the number of sides may vary.

Methods Students Might Use

- Multiply the number of triangles by three
- Create visual models with a picture of miniature triangles
- Count by threes

If students do not come up with these ideas, suggest them as possible solutions and have students evaluate them. Be sure that students see the benefit of organizing the information so that it is easy to locate. Encourage them to describe their solutions in terms of continuing a pattern or sequence.

Once students have commented on the different solutions and how useful they are, ask them how they would use their systems to find out how many sides 15 triangles have. Students may see that they could extend the sequence. They may also see that they could add the results for 10 and 5 or for any other combinations of 15. Take some time and have students try a few other

f.y.i.

This question was set up in such a way as to almost force students to think about using patterns. If the question had been just to determine how many sides four triangles had students could solve it one time with many methods. But, since the question asks students to create something that could be used many times, they can see how a pattern or a chart could be useful.

combinations for 15. Again, focus students' attention on how accurate and useful their methods are.

CONTINUE THE LESSON by having students solve two problems similar to the triangle problem. This time have them use squares and pentagons. Again, ask students to develop a system that will allow them or others to quickly and easily tell how many sides there are on 1–10 squares and 1–10 pentagons. When students have completed the problems, bring them together to review their methods. *Did anyone use a different method for these problems? What patterns do you see in your solutions?*

Extension

After observing your students as they solved the previous problems, you may think they are ready to try a more difficult problem that uses a more complex sequence involving doubling. If so continue the lesson by presenting the following scenario.

> **The owners of the Shape Company want to give out coupons to their customers. The owners have decided to base the number of coupons on the number of orders placed. Here is the pattern they set up for the first five orders a customer makes:**

Number of Orders	1	2	3	4	5
Number of Coupons	1	2	4	8	16

The students' task is to make a chart for the first ten orders. Have students work in pairs to make the chart. When students are finished, have them describe the sequence and how they determined what it is. (Sequence: 6th, 32; 7th, 64; 8th, 128; 9th, 256; 10th, 512) Then discuss the situation. *Is the owners' plan a good one? Why or why not?* As students discuss whether or not the idea of the coupons was a good one, make sure they look at what will happen if customers place even more orders than the ones shown on the chart.

Student Pages

Student pages 48 and 49 contain problems that can be solved using patterns.

Assessment

You observed students as they extended their understanding of number patterns and sequences in problem solving situations. They organized their thinking and applied different problem-solving strategies connecting patterns to lists or tables. They looked at the relationships between the numbers in sequences and predicted possible outcomes using the patterns they observed.

NCTM Standards Summary

Students used problem-solving strategies and connected to their knowledge of arithmetic as they analyzed problems, used patterns to solve problems, and made generalizations about patterns and relationships. They organized the information they generated in lists or tables and applied different operations to determine pattern rules and solve problems. They communicated as they shared their thinking with their group members and classmates, explaining how they had applied their strategies to the problems.

Answers

Page 48

1. 16, 20, 24, 28, 32, 36, 40
2. 4 sides
3. 40 sides
4. The rule is + 4.
5. • • • • •
   • • • • •
   • • • • •
   • • • • •
   • • • • •
6. Each figure has 1 more dot in each row and 1 more dot in each column than the previous figure.
7. 10 rows and 10 columns or 100 dots in all
8. ⠀⠀•
   ⠀⠀• •
   ⠀• • •
   • • • •
   • • • • •
9. Each figure has 1 more row than the previous figure. The new row has 1 more dot than the previous row.
10. 10 + 9 + 8 + 7 + 6 + 5 + 4 + 3 + 2 + 1 = 55 dots

Page 49

1. $0.44, $0.55, $0.77, $0.88, $1.10; Answers will vary.
2. 15 and 30
3. 5

Using Patterns to Solve Problems

Answer the questions. Use pattern blocks to help.

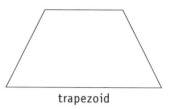
trapezoid

❶ Complete the chart.

Number of Trapezoids	Sides
1	4
2	8
3	12
4	
5	
6	
7	
8	
9	
10	

❷ How many sides does 1 trapezoid have?

_____

❸ How many sides do 10 trapezoids have?

_____

❹ Describe the pattern or state the rule.

_____

_____

_____

Use the pattern to answer the questions.

❺ Draw the next figure.

❻ Describe the pattern or state the rule.

_____

❼ How many dots will the tenth figure have? Explain how you know.

_____

❽ Draw the next pattern.

❾ Describe the pattern or state the rule.

_____

❿ How many dots will the tenth figure have? Explain how you know.

_____

Standard 2 Algebra

Using Patterns to Solve Problems

1 Complete the chart. Explain how you found the missing amounts.

Cost of 11-Cent Stickers

Number of Stickers	Cost
1	$0.11
2	$0.22
3	$0.33
4	
5	
6	$0.66
7	
8	
9	$0.99
10	

2 You are counting by threes to 30. Your friend is counting by fives to 30. Will you ever say the same numbers. If so, what numbers?

3 A store is giving away coupons with each order.
The chart shows how many coupons to give away.
How many coupons are given away with an order of 10 items?

Number of Items	1	2	3	4	5	6	7	8	9	10
Number of Coupons	1	1	2	2	3					

Relating Multiplication and Division

Introduction

Objective → Students will be able to write related multiplication and division sentences and use the relationship to solve problems.

Context → Students are familiar with the relationship between addition and subtraction. They have used multiplication facts and have investigated division in the context of grouping and sharing. Presenting this lesson early in a unit on division provides a basis for later work with one-digit divisors and the use of inverse operations for finding find the missing number in a number sentence.

NCTM Standards Focus

In this standards-based lesson, students explore the relationship between multiplication and division by examining number sentences and deriving a related division sentence from a multiplication sentence. Then they use this relationship to find the missing number in a number sentence.

Reasoning and Proof Students analyze the numbers and structure of equivalent multiplication and division sentences and use their observations to understand the relationship between the operations. As they develop an understanding of the relationship, students will become fluent in using the operations to solve problems and to check their solutions.

Representation Students represent multiplication and division problems by making drawings and writing number sentences. As they work on these activities, students will reinforce their understanding of the meaning of division and of how division and multiplication are related.

Connections Students will connect the inverse relationship between addition and subtraction to the similar relationship between multiplication and division. Division problems will be linked to real-world situations to reduce the level of abstraction in the lesson.

Teaching Plan

Materials → Student pages 54–55

INTRODUCE THE LESSON by presenting the following situation to the class.

> Carla baked 20 cookies. She wants to give each of four friends the same number of cookies. *How many cookies will Carla give to each friend?*

What operation could you use to find the answer to this problem? (Division) Tell students that if they think about their multiplication facts, they will realize they already know the answer.

Remind the students that when they solved a subtraction problem such as $7 - 3 = 4$, they could use the addition sentence $4 + 3 = 7$ to check to see if their answer was correct. *Why do you use addition to check subtraction?* (Because addition and subtraction are related or opposite operations.)

Write 6 ÷ 2 = 3 on the board. Ask students how they might check to see if this is a true sentence. (3 × 2 = 6) *What are the two related operations in these examples?* (Multiplication and division)

HAVE STUDENTS WORK in pairs. Ask students to draw a diagram or picture that illustrates the situation of sharing 20 cookies equally among four friends. Circulate among the pairs as they work and offer help if any students have difficulty getting started. If necessary, review the meaning of division as the operation that separates the whole amount into groups with the same number in each group.

When students have completed their drawings, have them compare theirs with another group. The drawings should be similar to the one shown.

20 cookies for 4 friends

Ask students to write a division fact and a multiplication fact that describes the problem they pictured. (20 ÷ 4 = 5; 4 × 5 = 20) Have students explain what the numbers in each sentence represent. Emphasize that in both sentences 20 stands for the total number of cookies, 4 stands for the number of groups (friends) and 5 stands for the number in each group (number of cookies each friend gets).

What does this tell you about multiplication and division? (They are related or opposite operations.) *How can knowing this relationship help you?* (You can rewrite a division problem as a multiplication problem and use what you know about multiplication to solve the problem or vice versa.)

PRESENT THE FOLLOWING SITUATION to the students:

> **While on a trip to the beach, each member of the Chavez family found 3 seashells. There were 18 seashells in all.** *How many Chavez family members were at the beach?*

Have students make a drawing to illustrate this problem. (Students will draw groups of 3 until they have a total of 18, or 6 groups of 3.) Write this multiplication sentence on the board: ____ × 3 = 18. Point out to students that a number is missing from this sentence. *What does the missing number stand for?* (The number of Chavez family members)

Ask students how this multiplication sentence can be rewritten as a division sentence. When the correct answer (18 ÷ 3 = 6) is suggested, write it on the board to make the visual comparison clear. *How are these two sentences similar?* (Each sentence uses the same numbers and the numbers, including the missing number, have the same meaning in each sentence.) *What is the missing number?* (6) *Which sentence did you use to find your answer?* (Students may suggest either sentence, depending on whether they find it easier to work with multiplication or division facts.) Summarize this part of the lesson by asking the following questions.

- *If you are given a multiplication sentence in which one of the numbers (factors) to be multiplied is missing, how can you find the missing number?* (Rewrite the problems as a division sentence and solve.)
- *Why can you use this method?* (Because division and multiplication are related or opposite operations.)
- *How can you check to see if the number you found by dividing is correct?* (By multiplying; 6 × 3 = 18)

If time allows, have students ask each other to find the missing numbers in other multiplication number sentences, such as 4 × ___ = 12 or ___ × 9 = 27. Be sure students understand that the missing number can be in either position. Have students record the given sentence, the completed sentence, and the related division sentence. Encourage students to use a wide variety of facts and not to repeat facts. This activity can also be carried out with the class divided into two teams with opponents taking turns giving and solving the missing number sentences.

Student Pages

Student page 54 provides exercises to review the meaning of division and gives students practice in writing sets of related facts. Student page 55 includes missing number exercises, applied problems, and an opportunity for students to create their own related-operations problems.

Assessment

You had opportunities to assess students' understanding of division and the relationship between division and multiplication as they made drawings and wrote pairs of sentences. Students' responses during the discussion of missing number problems also served as indicators of their proficiency in converting from one operation to another and in applying their understanding to solve problems. Additional items for evaluation were provided by the practice exercises on the student pages.

NCTM Standards Summary

By examining related multiplication and division sentences, students used their own thinking processes to deduce the relationship between the two operations. This approach made students active participants in their own learning and enhanced their understanding of the important inverse relationship. Representation using drawings and symbolism (number sentences) supported students' reasoning about the operations, helping them to focus on the similarities of structure and meaning of the numbers. Connecting the relationship between multiplication and division to students' prior knowledge about addition and subtraction helped them to draw on their intuition about the operations. Linking the problems to real-world situations provided a context so students could think more clearly about the meaning of each number and operation; reducing the level of abstraction and symbolic manipulation made the lesson less intimidating and created a better learning opportunity.

Answers

Page 54

1. $2 \times 4 = 8$, $4 \times 2 = 8$, $8 \div 2 = 4$, $8 \div 4 = 2$
2. $6 \times 5 = 30$, $5 \times 6 = 30$, $30 \div 5 = 6$, $30 \div 6 = 5$
3. $3 \times 7 = 21$, $21 \div 3 = 7$, $21 \div 7 = 3$
4. $24 \div 6 = 4$, $6 \times 4 = 24$, $4 \times 6 = 24$
5. $4 \times 8 = 32$, $32 \div 4 = 8$, $32 \div 8 = 4$
6. $45 \div 9 = 5$, $5 \times 9 = 45$, $9 \times 5 = 45$
7. Answers may vary.
8. Answers may vary.
9. Answers may vary.
10. Answers may vary.

Page 55

1. $28 \div 7 = 4$, 4
2. $24 \div 8 = 3$, 3
3. $15 \div 5 = 3$, 3
4. $42 \div 6 = 7$, 7
5. $64 \div 8 = 8$, 8
6. $9 \div 9 = 1$, 1
7. $12 \times 1 = 12$, $1 \times 12 = 12$, $12 \div 1 = 12$, $12 \div 12 = 1$; $6 \times 2 = 12$, $2 \times 6 = 12$, $12 \div 2 = 6$, $12 \div 6 = 2$; $3 \times 4 = 12$, $4 \times 3 = 12$, $12 \div 4 = 3$, $12 \div 3 = 4$
8. Answers may vary.

Relating Multiplication and Division

Write two multiplication facts and two division facts for each picture.

1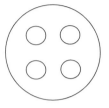

2

_____

_____

_____

_____

Write three other related facts.

3 $7 \times 3 = 21$

_____

_____

_____

4 $24 \div 4 = 6$

_____

_____

_____

5 $8 \times 4 = 32$

_____

_____

_____

6 $45 \div 5 = 9$

_____

_____

_____

Write two multiplication facts. Rewrite each as a division fact.

7 _____

8 _____

**Write two division facts. Rewrite each as a multiplication fact.
(Do not use the same facts as in exercises 7–8.)**

9 _____

10 _____

Standard 2 Algebra

Relating Multiplication and Division

Rewrite each multiplication sentence as a division sentence.
Find the missing number.

1 $7 \times$ _____ $= 28$ _____

2 $8 \times$ _____ $= 24$ _____

3 $5 \times$ _____ $= 15$ _____

4 _____ $\times 6 = 42$ _____

5 _____ $\times 8 = 64$ _____

6 $9 \times$ _____ $= 9$ _____

7 Suppose you were asked to arrange 12 desks so each row had the same number of desks.
Draw all the possible ways you could do this.
Write all the possible multiplication and related division sentences.

8 Write two word problems that require multiplication to solve.
Give your problems to a classmate.
Ask him or her to rewrite each as a division problem and solve.

_____   _____

_____   _____

_____   _____

_____   _____

_____   _____

Relating Fractions and Division

Introduction

Objective → Students will relate fractional parts of a set and division by identifying, using, and generalizing mathematical connections.

Context → Students have used the concept of division and have learned the basic division facts. They have identified fractions of a whole and of a set. They will continue to see fractions as a different way to show division and will use division when they solve problems involving fractions of a set.

NCTM Standards Focus

When students see mathematics as a set of isolated topics and concepts, they often struggle with the concept and meaning of fractions. In this standards-based lesson, students connect fractional parts with what they already understand about division. They study the patterns in a function table to help them generalize about using division to find a fraction of a set.

Connections Students link their knowledge of division to fractions of a set. They connect fractions of a whole to fractions of a set, understanding that both represent equal parts, whether of a whole object or a group of objects.

Representation Students use concrete materials to represent division and to find fractions of sets. They also use figures, including fraction notation, to represent the number of equal parts and the number in each part.

Teaching Plan

Materials → Student pages 60–61; two-color counters; other counters; small brown paper bags

HAVE STUDENTS WORK with a partner. Give each pair a paper bag with 15 counters. Ask them to show 8 counters, yellow side up. Then ask them to turn one-half of the counters red side up. After students have done this, write on the board $\frac{1}{2}$ of 8 = 4. Have students tell how they approached the problem and explain why half of 8 is 4.

Give a copy of student page 60 to each student. Explain that student pairs will use their counters to represent the grapes. They can start by putting 4 grapes in the lunch bag and filling in the first row of the chart. Each student should fill out the chart and answer the two questions below it. Let students know that they will share their answers and problem-solving strategies when the charts are finished.

Observe students as they work together. Ask how they figured out how many were half of the grapes for each number of grapes. *How do you know that 3 is half of 6?* Encourage students to explain the thinking they did to determine which operations or methods to use. Keep focusing students back on the fact that they are dealing with fractions of a set. *What do you know about fractions? What does one-half mean? How do you know your answers show equal parts?*

When students finish the chart, have them share their work in a group discussion.

Methods Students Might Use

- They might deal out the counters and partition them into two equal groups.
- They might use their knowledge of doubles to figure out how much each partner will receive.
- Relying on their knowledge of the twos times table, they might think $6 = 2 \times ?$, and solve for the unknown factor.
- They might divide by 2.

As students share their solutions and strategies, encourage them to restate their answers in terms of one-half; for example, one-half of 12 is 6. After a pair of students share their methods, encourage the rest of the class to respond. *Did anyone use a different method? How were your methods similar to each other?* Encourage students to try out the different methods and then tell which one they think is the easiest, fastest, or most sensible, and why.

f.y.i.

Two-color counters help students see 2 equal sets that make up a whole, giving them a concrete picture of what one-half looks like. You can use a variety of manipulatives for this activity. For example, have students cut out squares from colored construction paper and color one side a contrasting color.

What Might Happen . . . What to Do

Some students might be confused about fractions as both part of a whole and part of a set. For example, they know that $\frac{1}{2}$ is less than 1 and may wonder how $\frac{1}{2}$ can also be 6 ($\frac{1}{2}$ of 12). Emphasize that the set is 1 whole. Set out 12 items and draw a circle around them. Divide the circle in half, including 6 items in each half. Show students how their understanding of fractions of a whole works for fractions of a set.

THROUGH THIS DISCUSSION, help students to make connections between fractions and division. Help students see the efficiency of dividing the number of items in a whole set by the denominator of the fraction. Refocus students' attention on the symbolic expression, e.g., $\frac{1}{2}$ of 6 = 3. Bring out that if you divide the set into 2 equal parts, each part is one-half

----

of the set ($6 \div 2 = 3$). Continue asking students what they are dividing and how they know that division is a way to solve these problems.

Ask students to look for patterns in the chart. Bring out the idea that when the whole set grows by 2 grapes, the partners get 1 more grape each. Have students compare the whole sets of 4 grapes and 8 grapes. *What can you say about the relationship of the whole sets?* (8 is double 4.) *What about the half sets—the number of grapes each partner gets?* (4 is double 2.) *Suppose the whole set contained 16 grapes. How many grapes would each partner get? How can you use the chart to figure this out?*

Assess the students' comfort level as they alternate between division and multiplication. Students should be comfortable finding that, if one-half of 8 grapes is 4 grapes, then one-half of 16, which is double 8, should be double 4, or 8.

Ask students to keep page 60 out as they read and begin to work on student page 61. After they have completed the first two exercises, discuss how they used the chart on page 60 to figure out the answers. Encourage them to show how they solved the problems using relationships between the numbers. For example:

$\frac{1}{2}$ of $10 = 5$

$20 = 2 \times 10$, so

$\frac{1}{2}$ of $20 = 2 \times \frac{1}{2}$ of 10, or 2×5

$2 \times 5 = 10$

ALLOW STUDENTS TO SHARE their pictures or other ways of solving the problems. Encourage them to try each other's methods and then decide which way was easiest or fastest.

Have students continue with page 60. Observe them as they use counters to determine what $\frac{1}{3}$ of 3 equals. How do they approach the fraction one-third? Do they connect this task to the previous activity? Do they use division to solve the problem or to check their answers? As students finish the page, circulate and ask questions about their methods. Can they represent what they did using numbers? With the whole group, review students' solutions and how they used previously discussed methods and strategies.

Extensions

Some students may easily see the connection between fractions of a set and division. You might challenge them further by having them explore other fractions. Have them consider how a fraction like $\frac{3}{4}$ is different from $\frac{1}{4}$. Then have them work with fraction families and whole numbers. For example,

Find $\frac{1}{4}$, $\frac{2}{4}$, and $\frac{3}{4}$ of 8 and 16.
Find $\frac{1}{5}$, $\frac{2}{5}$, $\frac{3}{5}$, and $\frac{4}{5}$ of 10 and 20.

Encourage students to look for and describe patterns in the numbers. Have them tell how they can use division and multiplication to find multiple fractions of a set. (First divide the set by the denominator and then multiply the answer by the numerator.)

Student Pages

Student page 60 contains the table of wholes and halves for students to fill in. Student page 61 contains additional activities in which students look at patterns with $\frac{1}{2}$, explore $\frac{1}{3}$, and relate fractions to division.

Assessment

You observed students grapple with the problem of how to determine a fraction of a set. They applied their knowledge of division to an activity they first solved using concrete materials. You observed how well they understood that finding one-half is the same as partitioning a set into two groups, or dividing by 2. You further assessed the students' understanding of the relationships between a number and its half and multiples of the number and its half.

NCTM Standards Summary

Students connected the operation of division to finding fractions of sets as they noted, for example, that to find $\frac{1}{2}$ of a group of objects, you divide the number of objects by 2. They also connected to multiplication as they observed the relationships between numbers in a table of wholes and halves. They represented their understanding with concrete materials, drawings, and symbolic notation, or a combination of methods.

Answers

Page 60

1. Chart: $\frac{1}{2}$ of 4 = 2, $\frac{1}{2}$ of 6 = 3, $\frac{1}{2}$ of 8 = 4, $\frac{1}{2}$ of 10 = 5, $\frac{1}{2}$ of 12 = 6

2. Possible answers include: Divide the sets into two groups. Divide by 2.

3. Possible answers include: When you double the halves you get the whole sets. When the whole goes up by 2, the $\frac{1}{2}$ goes up by 1.

Page 61

1. 10; Possible answer: 20 is 2 × 10, $\frac{1}{2}$ of 10 is 5, so $\frac{1}{2}$ of 20 = 2 × 5 = 10

2. 12; Possible answer: 24 is 2 × 12; $\frac{1}{2}$ of 12 is 6; so $\frac{1}{2}$ of 24 = 2 × 6 = 12

3. $\frac{1}{3}$ of 3 = 1; Possible answer: I set out 3 counters. To find $\frac{1}{3}$, I divided: 3 ÷ 3 = 1.

4. $\frac{1}{3}$ of 3 = 1, $\frac{1}{3}$ of 6 = 2, $\frac{1}{3}$ of 9 = 3, $\frac{1}{3}$ of 12 = 4

5. Possible answer: When the whole goes up by 3, the $\frac{1}{3}$ goes up by 1.

6. Possible answer: $\frac{1}{3}$ means that the whole is partitioned into 3 equal parts. When you divide you break the whole into equal parts, so in both cases you divided a whole into 3 equal parts.

Relating Fractions and Division

Fill in the chart. Then answer the questions below.

❶ You and your partner have a lunch bag with some juicy grapes.
You are sharing the grapes equally, so each of you will get half of them.
How many grapes will each of you get?

Number of grapes in the lunch bag	$\frac{1}{2}$ of the grapes	Each person gets
4		grapes
6		grapes
8		grapes
10		grapes
12		grapes

❷ How did you figure out how many grapes each person gets?

❸ What patterns do you see in the chart?

Relating Fractions and Division

Use the chart on page 60 or draw a picture.

❶ What is $\frac{1}{2}$ of 20? _____
How did you figure it out?

❷ What is $\frac{1}{2}$ of 24? _____
How did you figure it out?

Use your counters.

❸ What is $\frac{1}{3}$ of 3?

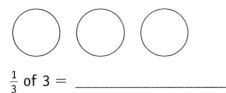

$\frac{1}{3}$ of 3 = _____
How did you figure it out?

**Fill in the chart. Use counters or draw pictures to help.
Then answer the questions.**

❹

Whole set	$\frac{1}{3}$ of the set
3	
6	
9	
12	

❺ What patterns do you see in the chart?

❻ How is finding $\frac{1}{3}$ of a number like dividing by 3?

Exploring Properties of Multiplication

Introduction

Objective → Students will understand the commutative property of multiplication and use this property to facilitate recall of multiplication facts.

Context → Students already understand the multiplication process with small whole numbers. This lesson comes in the middle of several lessons in which students practice multiplication facts. They have had experience with the commutative property of addition.

Exploring Properties of Multiplication

Learn

Here is the Order Property of Multiplication.

Charlene works 4 days a week for 2 hours each day.

To find how many hours she works, add or skip count by 2 on the number line.

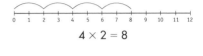

$4 \times 2 = 8$

$2 \times 4 = 8$

Bernard works 2 days a week for 4 hours each day.

To find how many hours he works, add or skip count by 4 on the number line.

4×2 and 2×4 both equal 8

> The Order Property of Multiplication tells you that you can multiply two numbers in any order and the answer will be the same.

Is the product of 4×3 the same as 3×4?
Yes, 4×3 and 3×4 both equal 12.

Discuss

1. Does the order property work for addition?
2. Does it work for subtraction?

NCTM Process Standards Analysis and Focus

The standards analysis examines how the process standards have been incorporated into the above lesson. By increasing the focus on three of the process standards, a more effective and meaningful lesson can be presented. The suggestions offered can help you to think about how this might be accomplished.

Representation The lesson represents multiplication as repeated addition and uses number lines to demonstrate that related multiplication facts produce the same product.

Suggestion → Have students create visual representations of multiplication facts by drawing rectangular arrays on grid paper. Rotating the arrays will produce the related multiplication array, demonstrating the commutative property of multiplication.

Practice

Use the number line to complete the multiplication sentences below.

```
+--+--+--+--+--+--+--+--+--+--+--+--+--+--+--+--+--+--+--+--+--+--+--+--+--+--+--+--+--+--+
0  1  2  3  4  5  6  7  8  9 10 11 12 13 14 15 16 17 18 19 20 21 22 23 24 25 26 27 28 29 30
```

1. $5 \times 3 = ?$ **2.** $3 \times 5 = ?$ **3.** $3 \times 2 = ?$

4. $6 \times 4 = ?$ **5.** $5 \times 5 = ?$ **6.** $3 \times 6 = ?$

7. $7 \times 2 = ?$ **8.** $3 \times 8 = ?$ **9.** $5 \times 6 = ?$

10. $4 \times 5 = ?$ **11.** $4 \times 3 = ?$ **12.** $4 \times 3 = ?$

13. $4 \times 6 = ?$ **14.** $2 \times 7 = ?$ **15.** $5 \times 7 = ?$

16. $8 \times 3 = ?$ **17.** $6 \times 5 = ?$ **18.** $8 \times 4 = ?$

19. $3 \times 9 = ?$ **20.** $4 \times 6 = ?$ **21.** $7 \times 4 = ?$

Problem Solving

22. There are 4 baseball cards in each pack. How many baseball cards will you have if you buy 5 packs?

23. Rosa wants to collect 28 baseball cards. How many packs will she need to buy?

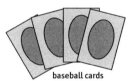

baseball cards

Communication

24. Describe the order property of multiplication. Use words and examples.

Connections The lesson makes a connection to the commutative property of addition, but there is little connection made to the actual use of the commutative property of multiplication in the exercises of the lesson.

Suggestion → Help students connect related facts to each other by identifying the two multiplication facts that represent each rectangular array. As they compare the two facts, students will see that while the product and the factors are the same, the order of the factors is reversed.

Reasoning and Proof The lesson asks students to give examples to support their answers to questions.

Suggestion → Direct students to make their own observations about how the order of the factors affects the product in multiplication. Encourage students to investigation multiplication facts and look for counter-examples of the commutative property. This will increase students' experience with this important property and reinforce its universal nature.

Problem Solving A few word problems at the end of the lesson provide some problem solving, but these problems do not help students develop an understanding of the commutative property.

Communication Students are asked to discuss the effect of changing the order of factors, addends, and the numbers in subtraction problems.

The teaching plan that follows shows how the suggestions for increasing the focus on the process standards can be implemented.

Revised Teaching Plan

Materials → Grid paper, several sheets per student; grid paper transparency for the overhead

BEGIN THE LESSON by displaying a rectangular array of 3 rows of 5 squares each on the overhead projector. Review the term *row* as needed. *This is called a rectangular array. How many rows are here? Is there a multiplication fact that we could use to help us find how many squares are in this array without counting them?* Students may offer $3 \times 5 = 15$ or $5 \times 3 = 15$. Although both are correct, record $3 \times 5 = 15$ on the overhead. *Let's use this one since we have 3 rows of 5 squares each.* You may wish to verify the accuracy of this equation by counting the squares with the class, either by ones or by fives. When students are learning a new concept, it's important for their sense of confidence to realize that each step makes good sense.

Rotate the rectangle, and encourage students to articulate the change that has occurred. *How many rows do we have how?* (5) *And how many squares are in each row?* (3). *We described the rectangular array with 3 rows of 5 squares with the multiplication fact $3 \times 5 = 15$. What multiplication fact should we use to describe this rectangle?* Students should be able to come up with $5 \times 3 = 15$ as the appropriate sentence. If students seem uncertain, try this transformation again a few times with other arrays such as 2×4 and 3×4. It's worth spending the time to be sure most students understand the process so they can focus on the underlying mathematics.

$3 \times 5 = 15$

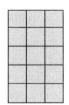

$5 \times 3 = 15$

HAVE STUDENTS WORK WITH their partners to create rectangular arrays on grid paper and identify two sentences that describe the two orientations of the same rectangle. Each student pair should make three or four arrays and identify two facts for each. If the activity is successful, it should be an "ah ha!" experience for many students as they discover that the product does not change when they reverse the order of the factors.

Invite student pairs to share their pairs of related facts with the class. Record their pairs of sentences on the board. *What pattern do you notice about the pairs of sentences on the board?* Introduce the terms *factor* and *product* if students don't already know them. *In discussing our discoveries in math, it helps to use just the right words. So let's use the terms* factor *and* product *as we talk about the patterns we see.* Students should be able to tell you that for each pair of number sentences the factors are the same but are in a different order and that the product is always the same.

What Might Happen . . . What to Do

Some students might make square arrays and notice that both multiplication facts are the same. This is a great opportunity to talk about these special-case numbers. *The product here is called a square number because the shape is a square. Square numbers are products of two factors that are the same.* Share your enthusiasm with students who make this important discovery, and ask them to be ready to share it with the class. If there's time, consider this additional reasoning challenge: *For the fact 4 × 4 = 16, 16 represents a square number. Can you name a multiplication fact with a product of 16 in which 16 does not represent a square number? (2 × 8 and 1 × 16)*

CONTINUE PROMPTING STUDENTS to make connections and use reasoning and proof. *Do you think you can find a pair of factors that would produce a different product when we reverse their order?* Students should be made aware that because they have found several examples of the commutative property, it doesn't mean it's always true. Suggest that students examine the different arrays they created to see if they can find an example in which the total number of squares changes when the array is turned. This challenge helps students to generalize about the reversibility of factors as they engage in trying to prove that the property always works by looking for an exception.

You may have students work individually, in pairs, or in small groups. Encourage them to try many pairs of factors. You may also choose to include calculators or limit the size of the factors to prevent calculation errors from distracting students during their search. An enjoyable activity like this offers a good opportunity to assess whether students have understood both the process of investigating this property and their comfort level with multiplication. Listen for and model the appropriate use of the terms *product* and *factor* as you interact with students. Stop the activity when students' enthusiasm wanes, and discuss the fact that no counter-examples could be found. If students think they have found one, help them check their work for calculation errors.

CONCLUDE THE LESSON by presenting the following situation.

> **Jorge knows that 3 × 7 = 21, but he always gets stuck on what 7 × 3 equals.** *What advice can you give Jorge to help him figure out 7 × 3?*

After a brief discussion, display a multiplication sentence on the board that was not recorded earlier. *Can you tell me another multiplication fact that uses the same factors?* Write several more multiplication facts on the board, and ask students to provide the related facts. Consider having students write each corresponding fact and hold it up for you to verify. *How can you use the discoveries we made today to help you learn the multiplication facts?*

Student Pages

Students should now be ready to complete exercises similar to those on the reduced student pages. Consider having students write the related multiplication sentence next the completed fact.

Assessment

This lesson provided ample opportunities to assess students' reasoning as they examined representations of multiplication facts to discover the commutative property. The various activities and discussions also allowed you to evaluate how comfortable students were in making connections between different representations of multiplication and how well they handled the more abstract work with multiplication facts.

NCTM Standards Summary

Representing multiplication facts in different ways enabled students to become more actively involved in learning about this new concept. Rotating rectangular arrays gave students an opportunity to make connections between those models and the commutative property of multiplication. This activity allowed them to observe for themselves that factors could be reversed without affecting the product. Students used reasoning and proof when they were asked if this concept could be generalized and whether they could find a counter-example.

Standard 3 **Geometry**

AT THE THIRD GRADE LEVEL, geometry includes work with symmetry, describing location, identifying two- and three-dimensional shapes, and analyzing geometric solids. Our lessons are derived from these important topics. They include a lesson that explores symmetry, a lesson on describing location, a lesson on identifying two- and three-dimensional shapes, and a lesson on determining attributes of geometric solids.

Three lessons model how the process standards can be used to teach content. A fourth lesson is a hypothetical textbook lesson that we have revised to be more standards based. These four lessons do not represent the entire curriculum, but rather provide glimpses of how, with a more concentrated effort to incorporate the process standards, better mathematics teaching and learning can be achieved.

One lesson we have chosen asks students to identify whether a two-dimensional figure is symmetrical or not and, if it is, to determine the line or lines of symmetry. This lesson is motivated by the process standard of reasoning and proof, as students make conjectures about the symmetry of a figure, then use paper-folding or a mirror device to test their theories.

In another lesson we have chosen, students read a map using the directions north, south, east, and west. The process standards of reasoning and proof and communication are important here, as students use logical thinking to give, receive, and interpret directions to find locations on a map.

A third lesson we have chosen requires students to identify three-dimensional shapes. By incorporating the process standards of reasoning and proof, communication, and representation, students will analyze various three-dimensional shapes and try to identify the distinguishing characteristics of each. They will discuss their ideas with classmates so that all can benefit from each other's observations.

The hypothetical textbook lesson we have chosen to revise has students determining the attributes of geometric solids. This lesson generally has students memorize definitions and identify figures. By incorporating the process standards of problem solving, reasoning and proof, and communication into the lesson, students discover for themselves the attributes of the different figures and create their own descriptions.

Standard 3 Lessons

Exploring Symmetry

Describing Location

Identifying Three-Dimensional Shapes

Determining Attributes of Geometric Solids

Exploring Symmetry

Introduction

Objective → Students will be able to identify and describe symmetrical figures and determine the lines of symmetry in two-dimensional figures.

Context → Students have identified and described two-dimensional shapes. After this lesson they will identify and describe three-dimensional shapes.

NCTM Standards Focus

Often students are not given opportunities to use representational methods to determine whether or not figures are symmetrical and to help them find the lines of symmetry. In this standards-based lesson, students use their ability to visualize shapes and their reasoning skills to make conjectures about symmetrical and non-symmetrical figures. Students use representations to verify their conjectures.

Reasoning and Proof Students make conjectures about whether certain two-dimensional shapes have symmetry or not. They verify their conjectures by folding paper or using a mirror device.

Representation Students make representations of both symmetrical and non-symmetrical shapes. They use the representations to determine lines of symmetry and to verify whether or not a shape is symmetrical.

Communication Students convince other students of their beliefs. They also respond to questions by the teacher as a means of developing techniques to determine whether or not there is a line of symmetry.

Teaching Plan

Materials → Student pages 74–75; small mirrors or mirror-type devices; tracing paper.

BEGIN THE LESSON by telling students that today they are going to work with symmetry. They are going to try to find some methods to determine if a shape is symmetrical. Since students have worked with symmetry in earlier grades, ask them to explain what it means for a figure to be symmetrical.

Have some students go to the board or overhead and make drawings to illustrate their ideas about symmetry. A symmetrical figure is one that can be folded in half so that each half is a mirror image of the other. The line along which the figure is folded is called a *line of symmetry*.

Now show students the following shapes on the board or on the overhead.

Ask if either of the figures is symmetrical, and if so, where the lines of symmetry are. Students should be able to tell that the rectangle is a symmetrical figure while the triangle is not. Ask students if the rectangle has more than one line of symmetry. They should be able to see that it has two lines of symmetry. Also, ask students how they could prove to their fellow classmates that a figure has a line of symmetry.

AS STUDENTS DISCUSS THEIR IDEAS, list their methods for telling if a figure is symmetrical. Have students discuss the merits of each method. If they do not list the following two methods, suggest them.

- Place a mirror on the line of symmetry. If the figure appears the same when looking at the paper and in the mirror, the figure is symmetrical along that line of symmetry. With this method it may help to trace the figure first so the students can compare the traced figure with what they see on the paper and in the mirror.

- Have students trace the figure. Then have them make the external lines of the figure dark so these lines can be seen through the tracing paper. Then fold the figure along the line of symmetry and see if the halves match.

Organize students in pairs and give each pair a copy of student page 74, a mirror device, and tracing paper. Tell them that first they need to determine whether or not the figure is symmetrical. If they think the figure has a line of symmetry, they should use one of the methods discussed above to confirm their belief. Have students draw the lines of symmetry with dotted lines so the lines can be recognized as different from the other lines in the figure. Instruct students to keep a record of their work. This should include both notes and their tracings.

What Might Happen . . . What to Do

- -

Some students might find it difficult to work with the irregular shapes presented in problems 5 and 6. Have these students continue to work with regular shapes before having them move on to irregular shapes.

While students are working, circulate around the room and discuss with them what they are doing. Ask them how they initially decide whether the figure is symmetrical. Ask them which test they will use to see if their ideas are correct. Ask them how they can be sure that a figure is not symmetrical. Also ask them what could be done to make the figure symmetrical. These questions will help students deepen their understanding of symmetry.

When students have completed page 74, bring them back together and have them discuss their results. They should tell whether or not each figure is symmetrical, how many lines of symmetry it has if it is symmetrical, and how they confirmed their conclusions. Make sure that students justify all their conclusions, including those where they decide a figure is not symmetrical. Justifying a conclusion that a figure lacks an attribute will help them develop their ability to reason. Students are often asked to show why something fits a condition, but rarely are they asked to back up their beliefs when they say something does not fit a condition.

Either or both of the following activities may be used to reinforce the concepts of symmetry.

Activity 1

Have students go through the uppercase letters of the printed alphabet and find the letters that have lines of symmetry and those that don't.

Activity 2

Have students put a rubber band down the middle of a geoboard. Using this as a line of symmetry, have one student make a figure on one side of the geoboard. Have another student complete the figure so that it is symmetrical.

Close the lesson by reviewing with students how they can decide if a figure is symmetrical. Assign student page 75 for additional class work or as homework.

Student Pages

Student page 74 contains shapes for students to use during the lesson. Student page 75 has additional shapes that students determine to be symmetrical or non-symmetrical.

Assessment

You had opportunities to assess students' grasp of the concept of symmetry as they determined whether or not a figure was symmetrical and as they identified lines of symmetry. You also listened and observed students as they convinced others of their ideas and reasoning. At the end of the lesson, you were able to assess the students' ability to state what it means when a figure is symmetrical and what a line of symmetry is. Student page 75 gave you a chance to evaluate a student's individual work.

NCTM Standards Summary

Students used reasoning and representations to show that certain shapes were or were not symmetrical. They recorded their methods of determining whether the shapes were symmetrical and used those to try to convince classmates of their beliefs.

Answers

Page 74
1. Not symmetrical.
2. Symmetrical—one line of symmetry.
3. Symmetrical—two lines of symmetry.
4. Not symmetrical.
5. Not symmetrical.
6. Symmetrical—one line of symmetry.

Page 75
1. Symmetrical—one line of symmetry.
2. Symmetrical—three lines of symmetry.
3. Not symmetrical.
4. Not symmetrical.
5. Symmetrical—one line of symmetry.
6. Not symmetrical.

Exploring Symmetry

Tell whether each figure is symmetrical or not.
If it is symmetrical, draw its lines of symmetry.

1

2

3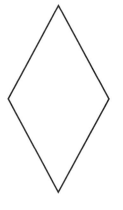

4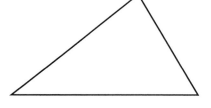

5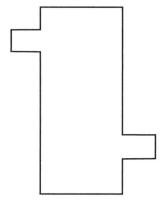

6

Exploring Symmetry

Name

**Tell whether each figure is symmetrical or not.
If it is symmetrical, draw its lines of symmetry.**

1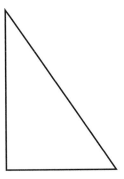

2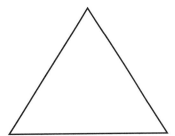

3

4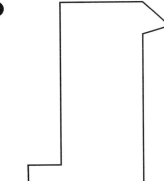

5

6

Standard 3 Geometry

Connect to NCTM Standards Third Grade → 75

Describing Location

Introduction

Objective → Students will read a map using north, south, east, and west. They will be able to locate objects and give directions.

Context → Students have had some experiences with maps. This is their first formal lesson on map reading. They have used mathematical terms to describe directions. Later in the year they will use the coordinate grid to identify movement in space.

NCTM Standards Focus

In this standards-based lesson, students use spatial reasoning in a real-world context. They connect abstract mathematical thinking and counting to the real world through the use of a map, which also connects mathematics to geography and social studies.

Reasoning and Proof Students use their understanding of the cardinal directions and of maps to interpret directions. They also use reasoning to give clues for finding a location; they use logical thinking as they analyze clues and use them to locate points on a map.

Communication Students give and receive directions for locating points on a map. They communicate specific locations using abstract terms.

Connections Students strengthen connections between their knowledge of directions and the real-world skills associated with reading maps.

Teaching Plan

Materials → Student pages 80–81; overhead of student page 80 (optional)

BEGIN THE LESSON by asking students to point out the directions north, south, east, and west. After making sure that everyone knows the directions, ask students when it might be important to know and use directions. If no one mentions that directions provide a common vocabulary that everyone can use to communicate where something is and how to get there, be sure to point this out.

Ask students if they or anyone they know has used a map. *Why was a map used?* Have a short discussion about specific instances in which a map was used and the results. Then focus on more general questions about when and why someone might use a map. Help students see that when using a map, a person needs to be able to locate where he or she is, as well as where he or she wants to go. Also ask students if they have seen the directions north, south, east, and west on maps and why the directions are there.

Tell students they will be looking at a map and using it to communicate directions to other students. Also, they will be using their reasoning skills to play a game where they try to determine the location a person is thinking of by asking *yes* or *no* questions about direction.

Pass out student page 80. First, have students orient their maps to north. Point out that on most maps north is up, east is to the right, south is down, and west is to the left. However, on some maps this may not be the case, so they should always check the directions.

Go over the map briefly, asking students to identify some points, such as streets and intersections. The following questions might help.

- *Which landmark is in the northeast corner of the map?* (The school)
- *Which street is farther west, Pratt Street or Green Street?* (Green Street)
- *Which street is one block east of Pratt Street?* (Lexington Street)

CONTINUE THE LESSON by telling students to imagine they are traveling on Third Avenue and want to find their way to a house on Pratt Street. Ask students how they would communicate which way to turn if they wanted to go on Pratt towards the school. Students may have a dilemma if they wanted to use *left* or *right* for directions because you did not tell them which way they were traveling on Third. Point this out and discuss with them when it might be better to use *left* and *right* and when it might be better to use *north, south,* etc.

What Might Happen . . . What to Do

Some students might have difficulty counting blocks on the map. Point out the similarities between the streets on the map and the numbers on a number line.	When you count the number of blocks traveled, you do not count the number of streets crossed, but the number of spaces between the streets.

f.y.i.

The use of maps and compasses to find directions is the basis of a popular sport. Orienteering has competitors race from specific location to location given a map, coordinates, and a compass. The sport combines the physical challenges of hiking with the mental stimulation of map reading.

Once you are satisfied that students can recognize and use north, south, east, and west, ask specific questions requiring students to interpret the map. You might ask the following questions.

- *You are walking between First Avenue and Second Avenue. The video store is on your right. In which direction are you traveling?* (North)

- *You are walking along Pratt Street, then turn onto Third Avenue on your way to Light Street. In which direction are you traveling?* (West)

- *You travel east along Second Avenue. You have just crossed Green Street. How many blocks away is Lexington Street?* (2 blocks)

- *What is the location of the school?* (At the intersection of Pratt Street and Third Avenue)

- *If you lived on Light Street between Third and Fourth Avenues, what direction would you travel to get to the school?* (North and east or south and east)

- *Beginning at the school, you walk two blocks south on Pratt Street and then go one block west. Where are you?* (First Avenue and Green Street)

STUDENTS CAN DO the next activity as a whole class or with a partner. This activity will require students to use their reasoning skills and communication skills in combination with their map skills. Tell students that you are thinking of a place or point on the map. The point can be an intersection or a building and must be located at an exact point. Tell students it is their goal to locate the place you are thinking about. They can ask only *yes* and *no* questions. For example, they can ask if the point is north of Second Avenue. While students can ask any *yes* or *no* question, encourage them to ask at least some that use the directions north, south, east, and west. When a student thinks he or she knows the answer, have him or her say what it is. To encourage reasoning and discourage guessing, tell students they need to state why they believe they have located the point.

To sum up the lesson ask students how they might show another person how to find directions on a map. You may wish to assign page 81, in which students write questions from a map as homework. You can have students bring their papers back and have them exchange papers. You could also have them give their papers to someone at home to answer the questions students wrote.

Student Pages

Student page 80 presents a map of a fictional town. This page is used in the first part of the lesson. Student page 81 presents a different map for students to use in writing and solving their own word problems.

Assessment

In the course of this lesson, you had the chance to assess students' understanding of directional symbols. Students' answers to the questions you posed about the map on student page 80 helped you to assess their ability to apply their spatial sense and counting skills in a real-world context. The game helped you see if students could apply their reasoning skill in a map-reading context.

NCTM Standards Summary

Students used logic and reasoning skills to map paths between locations and to identify locations. They communicated precise locations and directions using abstract terms. In doing so, they connected the abstract terms and directions to concrete locations shown on a map and also made connections to other content areas. They used their reasoning skills to find "mystery" locations.

Answers

Page 80
1. North
2. West
3. 2 blocks
4. At the intersection of Pratt Street and Third Avenue
5. North and east or south and east
6. First Avenue and Green Street

Page 81
Answers will vary depending on the questions students create about the map. Questions should cover the subjects listed.

Describing Location

Use the map to answer the questions about Millersville.

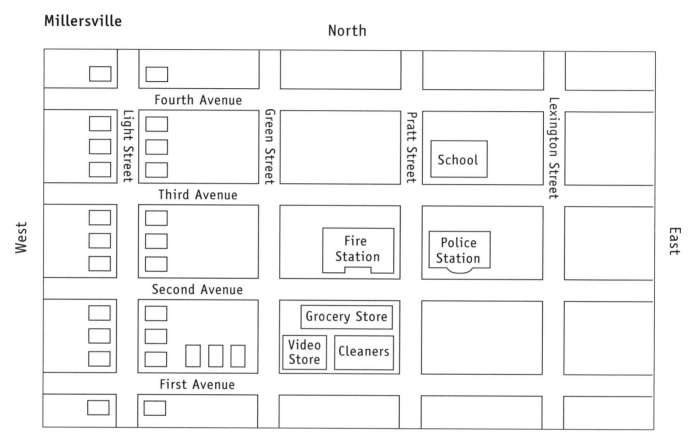

Millersville

North

West

East

South

❶ You are walking between First Avenue and Second Avenue. The video store is on your right. In which direction are you traveling?

❷ You walk along Pratt Street, then turn onto Third Avenue on your way to Light Street. In which direction are you traveling?

❸ You travel east along Second Avenue. You have just crossed Green Street. How many blocks away is Lexington Street?

❹ What is the location of the school?

❺ If you lived on Light Street between Third and Fourth Avenues, what direction would you travel to get to the school?

❻ Beginning at the school, you walk two blocks south on Pratt Street and then go one block west. Where are you?

Describing Location

Use the map to answer the questions about Kingston.

Write four questions about the map. Write one question about each of the subjects listed below. Put your answers on a separate sheet.

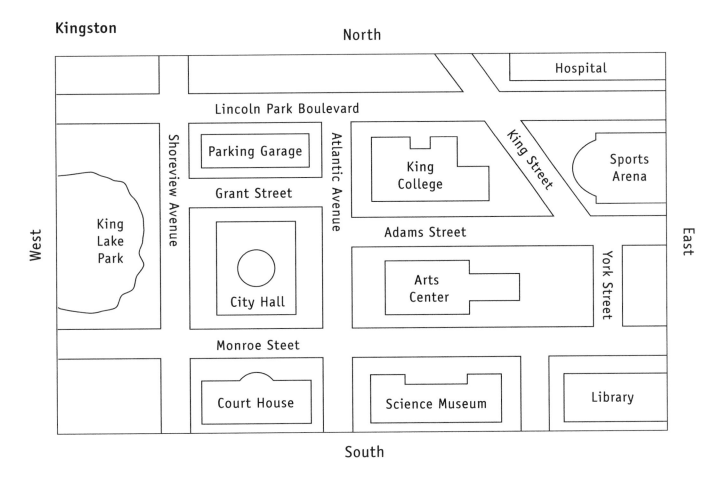

1 Write a question about map directions.

2 Write a question about where a landmark is located.

3 Write a question about how to get from one place to another.

4 Write a question about how far apart two locations are.

Identifying Three-Dimensional Shapes

Introduction

Objective → Students will describe and classify three-dimensional shapes.

Context → Students have described and classified two-dimensional shapes. They have explored three-dimensional shapes and their attributes informally. In this lesson, they will look at more formal definitions for three-dimensional shapes. Later they will solve problems involving three-dimensional shapes, including finding surface area and volume.

NCTM Standards Focus

In this lesson, students develop reasoning skills as they build new mathematical knowledge through the discovery and identification of the unique characteristics found in each member of a set of three-dimensional shapes. They use reasoning to communicate their new mathematical knowledge in the most concise form possible.

Reasoning Students analyze various three-dimensional shapes and identify the unique characteristics of each shape. They attempt to describe the shape as concisely as possible.

Communication Students use words and abstract symbols to identify different three-dimensional shapes and to communicate that information to others.

Teaching Plan

Materials → Student pages 86-87; collections of three-dimensional shapes (cube, rectangular prism that is not a cube, pyramid, sphere, cone, cylinder) in paper bags (one set per group of students)

PLACE ONE OF THE BAGS OF SHAPES at the front of the room. Tell students that you are going to have different students come up to the front of the room and put their hands in the bags. They are going to describe the objects by feel and see if the class can guess what the objects are. Depending on your class's knowledge of shapes, and how difficult you wish to make the activity, you may or may not wish to show or tell the group what shapes are in the bag.

Have a student come up and put his or her hand in the bag and grab an object to describe. Have the student focus on the characteristics of the object. If he or she says it is like a box, have him or her tell what that means: *What is it that makes it like a box?* Once students have guessed correctly, have the student pull the figure out. Review some of the clues, and ask students for other characteristics that might not have been mentioned. Repeat this until all the shapes have been identified.

Now turn the discussion to the attributes of the figures. Have students list the different types of attributes they saw in the different figures. Try to come up with a class definition for each characteristic. If the characteristics below have not been mentioned, suggest them yourself and list them.

What Students Might Say

- Edge: the line segment formed by the meeting of two faces
- Corner: the point where three edges meet
- Face: a flat two-dimensional part of the figure
- Shape of faces: the two-dimensional figures of each face

Hand out student page 86. Tell students that they will be working in small groups with the following figures: cube, rectangular prism, pyramid, sphere, cone, and cylinder. It may be helpful to leave a set labeled with each shape's name at the front of the room. Tell students they will need to look at each shape and fill out the information in the chart.

After students have completed the chart, tell them to add other attributes that describe each shape. The attributes they add do not have to be shared by all of the shapes. Encourage students to be as creative as possible in defining attributes. Suggest that they ask questions about each shape as a strategy for identifying possible attributes. For example: *Can I stack the shape? Does the shape roll? Does the shape come to a point?*

f.y.i.

Make sure students know that a cube is also a rectangular prism. They may best be able to relate this to the fact that, in the two-dimensional world, a square is also a rectangle.

This lesson is written with the assumption that the set of figures you are using has a rectangular pyramid.

What Might Happen . . . What to Do

Students might have problems with the fact that the sphere will have no edges, corners, or faces, and the cone and the cylinder will have no edges. Have students review the definition of edge as two faces meeting. Ask them if they can find two faces that meet. Again, they may be confused since there is a surface to some of the figures, but it is not a face. Make sure they understand that a face is a flat surface.

WHEN STUDENTS HAVE FINISHED, spend a few minutes reviewing what they have done. Their work needs to be accurate for them to complete the next assignment. Give students a copy of page 87. Tell students they are to come up with a definition or description of each of the shapes. Tell them that the class will test their definitions by having them read the definition and seeing if students can determine what the figure is.

Let students work either in pairs or individually to complete this activity. Encourage them to refer to their charts and to the figures. As you circulate, read their definitions and ask them questions, such as: *How would someone know you are not describing a cube?* When students are finished, call them back together to discuss their definitions or descriptions.

Have a student read a description and see if the class can identify the figure that the student has described. Also, ask questions that focus on students' reasoning and reinforce their knowledge of the figure. For example: *How do we know that isn't a cylinder? What would we have to change about the description to make it one for a pyramid?*

AFTER YOU HAVE SPENT SOME TIME on this, create a list on the board of descriptions that the class and you feel will be helpful for the students to use. Consider having a group of students make this list into a poster.

If time permits, have students create riddles that they can ask the class about the figures. For example: *I have more faces than either edges or corners and I can sit on either end. What am I?* (Cylinder)

Student Pages

Student page 86 presents a chart of three-dimensional shapes and their attributes. Students must fill in information to complete the chart and thoroughly describe each shape on the list.

Student page 87 provides space for students to write their definitions of shapes.

Assessment

You were able to assess students' understanding of shapes as they described characteristics and tried to guess the shapes. Also, you saw if students understood the characteristics of shapes as they tried to create definitions of shapes.

NCTM Standards Summary

Students used reasoning skills as they analyzed various three-dimensional shapes and identified each shape's unique characteristics. They used words and symbols to communicate and represent this information in definitions.

Answers

Page 86

1. Cube: 12 edges, 8 corners, 6 faces
2. Rectangular prism: 12 edges, 8 corners, 6 faces
3. Pyramid: 8 edges, 5 corners, 5 faces
4. Sphere: 0 edges, 0 corners, 0 faces
5. Cone: 0 edges, 0 corners, 1 face
6. Cylinder: 0 edges, 0 corners, 2 faces

Page 87
Answers may vary.

Identifying Three-Dimensional Shapes

Look at the shapes. Complete the table.

Shape	Number of edges	Number of corners	Number of faces
❶ Cube			
❷ Rectangular prism			
❸ Pyramid			
❹ Sphere			
❺ Cone			
❻ Cylinder			

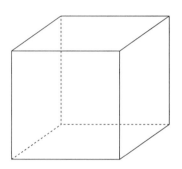

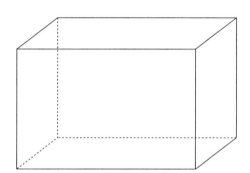

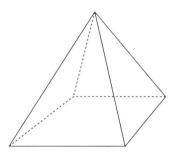

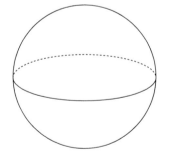

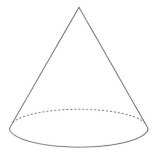

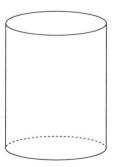

Identifying Three-Dimensional Shapes

Describe each shape.

❶ Cube

_____

_____

❷ Rectangular Prism

_____

_____

❸ Pyramid

_____

_____

❹ Sphere

_____

_____

❺ Cone

_____

_____

❻ Cylinder

_____

_____

Determining Attributes of Geometric Solids

Introduction

Objective → Students will identify cones, spheres, cylinders, cubes, prisms, and pyramids.

Context → This lesson occurs in a geometry unit after a study of the number of sides and angles in polygons. The unit continues with an introduction to area and volume.

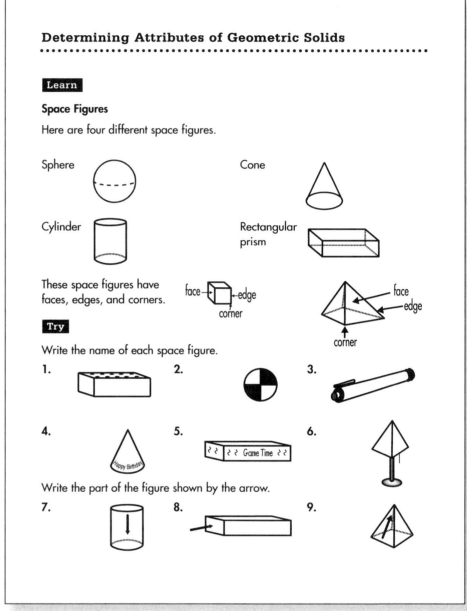

Determining Attributes of Geometric Solids

Learn

Space Figures

Here are four different space figures.

Sphere

Cone

Cylinder

Rectangular prism

These space figures have faces, edges, and corners.

face → edge

corner

face edge

corner

Try

Write the name of each space figure.

1.   2.   3.

4.   5.   6.

Game Time

Write the part of the figure shown by the arrow.

7.   8.   9.

NCTM Process Standards Analysis and Focus

The standards analysis examines how the process standards have been incorporated into the above lesson. By increasing the focus on three of the process standards, a more effective and meaningful lesson can be presented. The suggestions offered can help you to think about how this might be accomplished.

Problem Solving Activities involve naming three-dimensional figures, faces, and edges. Problem solving is not involved.

Suggestion → **Shift the focus from providing definitions for students to memorize and then use to identify figures to having students examine geometric solids and determine the attributes each figure possesses. Creating their own descriptions of these figures will help students focus**

· ·

Try

Name the space figure for each object.

1.

2.

3.

4.

5.

6.

Name each part of the figure shown by the arrow.

7.

8.

9.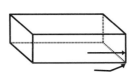

10. What space figure might you use with ice cream?

11. What space figure might soup come in?

12. What space figure might new shoes come in?

13. What space figure might you use to play soccer?

on the specific features used to classify these three-dimensional figures.

Reasoning and Proof Distinguishing the attributes of three-dimensional figures and having students explain how they recognize figures are limited to a brief suggestion in the teacher notes.

Suggestion → Have students verify their descriptions of figures by checking them against various representations.

Have students make comparisons between different geometric solids. Encourage students to identify solids from clues about their attributes to reinforce understanding of the features associated with each figure.

Communication Most questions prompt one-word responses. Opportunities for meaningful discussion are limited.

Suggestion → Encourage discussion in both small- and large-group settings to help students clarify terms and confirm their understanding of the attributes that distinguish figures from one another.

Representation Geometric solids are represented by three-dimensional drawings. The teacher notes suggest that students examine models and find pictures of figures in magazines and outline them.

Connections Teacher notes suggest that students name familiar items with shapes that conform to descriptions of three-dimensional shapes. Connecting to prior knowledge in identifying figures is not part of the lesson.

The teaching plan that follows shows how the suggestions for increasing the focus on the process standards can be implemented.

Revised Teaching Plan

Materials → Sets of geometric solids such as geoblocks plus an assortment of familiar objects that have shapes representative of cubes, rectangular prisms, square pyramids, triangular pyramids, cylinders, cones, and spheres, one set for each group of students; pictures or drawings of two- and three-dimensional shapes

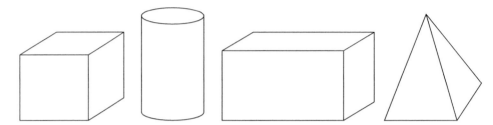

To begin the lesson, have students form groups and provide each group with a set of geometric solids. Tell students that they are to examine the solids and compile a list of the qualities or attributes that describe each item. Explain that the figures they have been given are called three-dimensional because they have length, width, and height. Demonstrate how you can move your hand around, under, and over the figure. Compare that with two-dimensional shapes such as drawings of squares, circles, and triangles, which have only length and width. Ask students to give examples of both two-dimensional and three-dimensional items to make sure they can distinguish between them.

Introduce the geometric solids one at a time. As you display each shape, identify it by name. Have students select a corresponding figure from their sets, hold it up, and repeat its name. Record the name of the solid on the board and place a picture of the figure under its name to serve as a reference for students as they work.

What Might Happen . . . What to Do

Making the distinction between a two-dimensional figure and a three-dimensional figure that appears to be a flat is a difficult concept. Students might think a piece of notebook paper is a two-dimensional item, but, in fact, that piece of paper has three dimensions—you can move over, under, and around it. Even when on a desktop, a piece of paper is still a three-dimensional object because it has thickness, albeit, not very much thickness.	Explain that the paper itself is three-dimensional, while a drawing of a rectangle on the sheet of paper is two-dimensional. The paper serves as the plane on which the two-dimensional drawing appears. Check for understanding by listing both flat three-dimensional objects, such as paper and a desk-top, and two-dimensional items, such as a drawing or a photo, and asking for a "thumbs-up, thumbs-down" vote from students about which are which.

START WITH A CUBE. Model the vocabulary that you will expect students to use during their investigation of attributes. Explain that each flat side of the cube is a plane and is called a face. Point out that all of the objects on their tables have faces. As they list information about each figure, students should be sure to include information about its faces. *How many faces does a cube have? How can we keep track as we count?* Count the 6 faces on the cube with the students, pointing to each face as you count and modeling a strategy for keeping track.

Next, ask students to find a place on the cube where two faces, and only two faces, meet. Explain that that place is called an edge. *How many edges does a cube have? How shall we keep track as we count?* Count edges with students, pointing to each, to confirm that all 12 edges are identified.

Then ask students to find a place where more than two faces come together. Explain that this place is called a corner or vertex. *Is a vertex also an edge? Why or why not?* (No. Three faces meet at a vertex; only two faces meet at an edge.) Confirm that there are 8 corners or vertices by counting with students. Model using precise language to help students distinguish and describe attributes as they investigate.

Record the attributes of a cube on the board in an organized way. *We know the cube has 6 faces, 8 edges, and 8 corners. What else do you notice about the cube?* Encourage students to be as explicit as possible as they describe the solid. Discuss possible ambiguous statements such as "it's square" to clarify what students are seeing. *What part is square?* (Each face) *Let's write that the cube has 6 square faces.*

DIRECT GROUPS OF STUDENTS to describe each shape and to include as much information as they can. Depending on time and the manipulatives available, you might have all groups describe each shape, or you might have each group focus on two or three. As you circulate, ask questions that focus on the problem-solving aspect of this activity. *How do you know you've found all of the attributes? Your description for this shape is a lot like your description for that one. Can you add more to show the differences between them?*

Invite individual groups to share their descriptions with the class. As they present their information, prompt students to incorporate the terminology introduced earlier. Instruct the class to listen carefully, evaluate each description, and suggest additions or words that might be eliminated because they are incorrect, ambiguous, or unnecessary. Record agreed-upon definitions in chart form on the board for students to copy.

Shape	Faces	Edges	Corners	Notes
cube	6 squares	8	8	all edges same length
square pyramid	4 triangles + 1 square	8	5	4 triangles same size
triangle pyramid	4 triangles	6	4	

NEXT, ASK STUDENTS TO COMPARE attributes of different solids. Encourage students to connect plane geometry with the figures they describe. *Compare the number of circular faces on a cylinder with those on a cone.* (A cylinder has two faces and a cone has only one.) *How are the triangular pyramid and the square pyramid the same or different?* (A triangular pyramid has 4 faces; all are triangles. A square pyramid has 5 faces; four are triangles and one is a square.)

Ask questions to help students organize their thinking. *Are cubes also rectangular prisms?* (Yes.) *Why?* (Both have 6 faces, 8 edges, and 8 corners, and the faces are all rectangles since squares are also rectangles.) *Are all rectangular prisms also cubes?* (No, a cube has only square faces.) *What do you notice when you compare the edges and vertices of rectangular prisms and cubes?* (All edges of a cube are the same length. That is not necessarily the case for rectangular prisms.)

CLOSE THE LESSON with the "Name Me" game. Ask students to write clues that will identify one of the geometric solids from the lesson. Each clue should be short and describe only one attribute. Clues should be given one at a time. Remind students to use appropriate terminology in their clues.

Here are two different sets of clues to describe a square pyramid.

I have 5 faces.	I have 5 vertices,
Four of my faces are triangles.	I have 8 edges.
My base is a square.	Four of my faces are triangles.
I have 5 corners or vertices.	I have 5 faces in all.
I have 8 edges.	My base is a square.

Student Pages

Students should now be ready to complete exercises similar to those on the reduced student pages.

Assessment

As small groups examined solids to create descriptions of their attributes, you were able to observe whether students were solving problems, applying reasoning, and communicating their ideas. Class discussion provided an additional opportunity to check students' understanding of the lesson concepts.

NCTM Standards Summary

Students were involved in problem solving as they examined, compared, and reasoned about the attributes that distinguish various geometric solids. Being able to handle solid figures allowed students to verify their thinking. Students were challenged to organize information and communicate their findings using precise terminology. Small-group and whole-class discussions promoted communication of ideas and reinforced students' understanding of the features that identify solids.

Standard 4 **Measurement**

AT THE THIRD GRADE LEVEL, measurement includes a lot of work with measuring using standard and non-standard units, finding the perimeter and area of two-dimensional figures, estimating and measuring capacity, and concepts of time. Our lessons are derived from these important topics. They include a lesson on using standard and nonstandard units to measure volume, a lesson on finding the perimeter of a figure, a lesson on estimating and measuring capacity, and a lesson on calculating elapsed time.

Three lessons model how the process standards can be used to teach content. A fourth lesson is a hypothetical textbook lesson that we have revised to be more standards based. These four lessons do not represent the entire curriculum, but rather provide glimpses of how, with a more concentrated effort to incorporate the process standards, better mathematics teaching and learning can be achieved.

One lesson we have chosen has students measure volume using nonstandard and standard units. Students are often just given a formula for volume and some practice problems in which to use it.

In this lesson, reasoning and proof and connections are emphasized as students determine that using standard units is more accurate and consistent than using nonstandard units. Students also begin to see a relationship between length, width, and height and the volume of a box.

Another lesson we have chosen has students find the perimeter of a figure by counting units. Through the process standards of problem solving, representation, and communication, students use nonstandard and standard units to measure perimeter and, through discussion, they realize that using standard units offers better results.

A third lesson we have chosen has students estimating and measuring capacity. In this lesson, students use problem solving, communication, and connections to try to determine how much water different containers will hold, based on adding only one cup of water to each container. Through discussions of their estimates, students develop a better sense of capacity.

The hypothetical textbook lesson we have chosen to revise is one that has students calculate elapsed time. Through better incorporation of the process standards of communication, reasoning and proof, and representation, students are able to understand and accomplish more than by just working with 15-minute increments. By allowing students to represent the time on clocks with moveable hands, and by providing opportunities for students to communicate their strategies, students can develop their own methods for calculating elapsed time. This is important since there is no one "best" way to calculate elapsed time.

Standard 4 Lessons

Using Standard and Nonstandard Units

Exploring Perimeter

Investigating Capacity

Calculating Elapsed Time

Using Standard and Nonstandard Units

Introduction

Objective → Students will measure volume in nonstandard and standard units, and determine that a standard unit is preferable.

Context → Students have measured length using both nonstandard and standard units of measure. This may be their first exposure to finding volume. They will go on to use the formula for volume of rectangular solids.

NCTM Standards Focus

Often, students' introduction to volume involves applying the formula $V = lwh$ to a figure with given dimensions. This standards-based lesson uses hands-on experience with concrete objects to help students understand the idea of volume. Students use nonstandard units of measure to find the volumes of different-sized boxes. Then, using centimeter cubes, students estimate and measure the volume of the boxes. Students concretely connect the relationship of length, width, and height to finding volume, establishing an understanding for eventually dealing with the formula.

Reasoning and Proof As they work with nonstandard units to determine volume, students use reasoning to develop methods to solve the problems. When they move to standard cubic units of measure, they confirm that the results are both more accurate and more consistent.

Connections When students fill the base of a box with cubic units, they connect the relationship of length, width, and height to the total volume of the box. They also connect to previous work with arrays and multiplication.

Teaching Plan

Materials → Student pages 100–101; identical sets of 2–4 small, sturdy rectangular boxes in different sizes (e.g., jewelry boxes, small toothpaste or raisin boxes, plastic staple boxes), 1 set for each group of students; marking pens; dry kidney beans or white northern beans; small marbles; centimeter cubes; centimeter ruler; chart paper

OPEN THE LESSON with a brief discussion. *What have you learned about measuring lengths of different objects? What do you have to do to get accurate measurements?* Ask students to recall experiences they have had measuring with nonstandard units. Guide the discussion to the idea that using a standard unit such as centimeters makes it likely that different people measuring the same object will get the same answer. This is because centimeters are all exactly the same length and are the same around the world.

Hold up 2 of the boxes you've collected, and set out a container of beans. *Which of these boxes do you think would hold more beans?* Tell students they are going to work in groups to explore volume, the measure of how much a shape will hold. Encourage them to look for ways they can connect what they already know about measurement to this exploration.

ARRANGE STUDENTS IN GROUPS. Give each group a set of boxes and a generous supply of both beans and marbles. Explain that the beans and marbles are going to serve as units of measure for the volumes of the different boxes. Have the students refer to student page 100. Select one box. Have each group locate the same-size box and label it with a 1. Do the same for the rest of the boxes. Then have students answer the first set of questions on page 100. When students have finished, ask for a show of hands to get their answers, and ask them to explain the reasoning behind their choices.

Have students continue with page 100 by filling Box 1 with beans, then counting the beans and recording the number. They should keep going until they have measured the volumes of all the boxes in both beans and marbles. While students are working, circulate around the room looking for the different strategies they use. When filling the boxes with marbles, students may find it difficult to fill the box evenly. Watch for their discussions as to whether they should leave the box slightly underfilled or slightly overfilled.

f.y.i.

Be sure to choose *small* boxes, as even a large toothpaste box will require hundreds of beans to fill and lots of time counting. The groups of students should have identical boxes so that they can accurately compare the volume.

What Might Happen . . . What to Do

Some students may have trouble keeping track while counting the beans. Suggest that students can arrange the beans in groups of 10, for example, so if they lose count, they won't have to start from the beginning. When they have all the beans in groups, they can skip-count by tens to get the total.

RECORD EACH GROUP'S results for all the boxes on chart paper and post the chart where students can study the figures. They will quickly see that there is a wide range of results. Ask students to answer the last question on student page 100 and then discuss these questions:

- *How are all the groups' measurements alike? How are they different?*
- *Is it clear which box holds the most beans? How about the most marbles?*
- *Does the box that holds the most beans also hold the most marbles?*
- *Would it be easy to compare the volume of a box filled with beans and the volume of a box filled with marbles? Why or why not?*

- *Are beans and marbles good units for finding volume? Why or why not?*
- *What might be a better unit for measuring volume?*

CHALLENGE STUDENTS TO THINK about choosing a standard measurement unit that will fill all the empty space in the box. If no one offers the idea of using cubes, hold up a centimeter cube. *Would this cube be a good unit for measuring the volume of the boxes? Why or why not?* Students should quickly see that cubes could fill all the empty space in the boxes.

Give each group of students a centimeter ruler and a supply of centimeter cubes. Have students measure a cube and determine that each side is 1 centimeter long. Explain that a cube that measures exactly 1 centimeter on each side is a unit of measure: 1 cubic centimeter. Have students put together 4 cubes, 6 cubes, and so on, to make rectangular solid figures. Ask them to give the volume of each figure in cubic centimeters.

Ask students to explain why centimeter cubes are a better way to measure volume than beans or marbles, besides the fact that they fit the space of the box better. *What is confusing about stating the volume of something as 252 beans?* Help students to see that we use standard units because everyone agrees on their size. That means that anywhere in the world, 252 cubic centimeters means the same volume.

DEMONSTRATE HOW STUDENTS can use the centimeter cubes to fill the base of one of the boxes. Students will probably see that even with cubic units, there is still some empty space. Discuss the fact that this measurement will not be perfect, but ask students to see how measuring with cubes compares to measuring with beans or marbles. Ask them how they might use the filled floor of the box to figure the total number of cubic centimeters the box will hold. Discuss the ideas they offer.

Direct students to student page 101. Have them work in their groups to complete the page. As they work, circulate to watch their approaches and listen to their ideas. Encourage them to try their classmates' ideas for estimating volume. As appropriate, encourage them to connect the task of measuring in cubic units to what they know about measuring length, width, and height, constructing arrays, and using repeated addition or multiplication.

f.y.i.

Depending on the boxes you use, two different-shaped boxes might share the same volume. If this occurs, you can have a class discussion about different shapes having the same volume. You can demonstrate this by using the same number of cubes to construct two or more different-shaped rectangular solids.

On a new chart, record the results from each group for the volumes of the boxes in cubic centimeters. There should be very little discrepancy in the results this time around. Have students discuss the reasons for any discrepancies that show up. For example, one group may have decided to put in a layer of cubes that came slightly above the top of the box, while another stopped with the layer that was slightly below the top of the box. Sum up the lesson by asking students to explain what units are best to measure volume and why.

Student Pages

Student page 100 is a recording sheet for the volumes of the boxes in beans and marbles. Student page 101 has students first estimate, then record, the volumes of the boxes in cubic centimeters. Both pages also ask students for a written response to a critical thinking question.

Assessment

While students worked in groups to fill the boxes with beans and marbles, you noted their discussions about the empty spaces and irregularities of the measuring materials. During the discussion, you could assess students' understanding of the reasons for discrepancies when they measured volume in beans and marbles, and the value of using standard cubic units. You then observed their techniques for estimating the volume of each box. Finally, you assessed whether students understood how to measure volume using centimeter cubes.

NCTM Standards Summary

Students used both nonstandard and standard measurement units to find the volumes of different boxes. Through their experience with different concrete materials, they reasoned that the most accurate way to measure volume is with cubic units. They confirmed that when they used cubic units, the different groups measurements were consistent. As they worked to estimate and measure volume with centimeter cubes, students had the opportunity to make connections to measuring length, width, and height, as well as to building arrays and using multiplication.

Answers

Page 100
Answers will vary.
Writing question: Students should note that there was a wide range of results. They may also note that the reason for the wide range is the irregularity of the shapes and sizes of the materials.

Page 101
Answers will vary.

Using Standard and Nonstandard Units

Look at boxes 1, 2, 3, and 4. Answer the questions.

1 Which box do you think will hold the **most** beans? _____

2 Which box do you think will hold the **most** marbles? _____

3 Which box do you think will hold the **fewest** beans? _____

4 Which box do you think will hold the **fewest** marbles? _____

5 Fill each box with beans. Count the beans, and record the total for each box.

6 Now fill each box with marbles. Count the marbles, and record the total for each box.

	Beans	**Marbles**
Box #1	_____	_____
Box #2	_____	_____
Box #3	_____	_____
Box #4	_____	_____

7 Compare your results with the other groups. What did you find out?

_____

_____

_____

_____

Standard 4 Measurement

Using Standard and Nonstandard Units

Look at boxes 1, 2, 3, and 4.

❶ Which box do you think will hold the **most** centimeter cubes? _____

❷ Which box do you think will hold the **fewest** centimeter cubes?_____

❸ Estimate the number of centimeter cubes each box will hold.
You may put one layer of cubes in the bottom of the box.
Write your estimate below.

❹ Fill each box with centimeter cubes.
Count the cubes. Record the actual volume of each box.

	Estimate	**Actual**
Box #1	_____ cubic centimeters	_____ cubic centimeters
Box #2	_____ cubic centimeters	_____ cubic centimeters
Box #3	_____ cubic centimeters	_____ cubic centimeters
Box #4	_____ cubic centimeters	_____ cubic centimeters

❺ Explain how you made your estimates. How could you have made better estimates?

_____

_____

_____

_____

Exploring Perimeter

Introduction

Objective → Students will determine the perimeter of given figures by counting units and will realize the importance and efficiency of using standard units.

Context → Students have had experiences with linear measurement using both non-standard and standard units of measure. They will go on to derive a formula for finding perimeter.

NCTM Standards Focus

In this standards-based lesson, students apply their experiences with linear measurement to find the perimeter of various figures. Through hands-on measuring activities, they see that to determine the perimeter of a figure, you must measure the lengths of the outlining sides of the figure. They do not deal with the formula for determining perimeter as they might do traditionally. Rather the focus is on counting units to develop an understanding of the formula when it is encountered.

Problem Solving When students discover a disparity in different groups' measurements of the perimeters of given figures, they look for a way to standardize the measure so they can agree on their results.

Representation Students represent measurements first with different nonstandard units and then with standard units, and discover the efficiency of using standard units. They represent the perimeter of a figure by counting the units around the figure.

Communication Students discuss the different results they get measuring with nonstandard units and the importance of using standard units. They learn and use the new vocabulary for this lesson.

Teaching Plan

Materials → Student pages 106–107; transparencies of pages 106 and 107; masking tape; overhead projector; overhead 1-inch grid paper; color tiles; chart paper

Preparation → Use masking tape to make 2 irregular figures on the floor in the hall or gym that are proportional to the figures on page 106.

BEGIN THE LESSON by asking students how they would measure a line. *What tool or tools would you use? What do you need to know to help you decide?* Continue this discussion until students understand that it's important to select the right tools and units of measure to fit each measurement task. *How might you measure the length of the school yard? The width of a paper clip?*

Divide the class into two groups and gather around the two tape figures you've constructed. Have students look at student page 106 as you explain that each of them should measure the distance around, or *perimeter*, of each figure by using their own feet. Ask a volunteer to demonstrate by walking heel-to-toe along one side of a figure as you count the steps. After measuring each side, they should record their measurement next to that side of the figure on the student page. Establish the concept that when they walk *around* a figure they are finding its perimeter.

PLACE A TRANSPARENCY of page 106 on the overhead. Ask one group to give you their measurements for each side of the first figure. Record these numbers on the transparency. Ask the other group to give you their measurements for the second figure, and record them. *How can you use all this information to find the perimeter of each of these figures?*

Students may bring up the following points:

- Some students may feel that their own measurements should be used. They will suggest adding their measurements for the sides of the figures. For example, Malia's measurements for Figure 1 are 15, 9, 6, 12, and 6 of Malia's feet. $15 + 9 + 6 + 12 + 6 = 48$. So the perimeter of Figure 1 is 48 Malia's feet.

- Other students may suggest looking for the most common measure for each side. With anywhere from 10 to 15 measurements per side, it is probable that there will be some identical measurements.

- Some students will be troubled by the discrepancy in the measurements and insist that the figures be measured with a standard unit.

The point of this discussion is to show the need for a standard unit of measure in cases where it's important to reach agreement. *Does it matter if we all agree on the perimeter of these figures? What if the figures were on plans for building a model house? Then would it be important that we agree?* Students should see that sometimes using a standard unit of measure is critical to the success of a project.

Place a transparent sheet of 1-inch grid paper on the overhead. Using color tiles, construct a shape with 5 of the tiles. Be sure that at least one edge of each tile fits against the edge of another tile. You may use one of the figures shown on student page 107 or create a different one. Explain that each side of a square on the paper and each side of a tile is 1 inch.

f.y.i.

The tape figures will be measured in nonstandard units (students' feet). You may want the students to go back and measure them in standard units at the end of the lesson.

f.y.i.

This lesson focuses on students' understanding that you can count units around the outside of a figure to determine its perimeter. Therefore, the emphasis of the teaching should be on counting units of measure, not deriving a formula for finding perimeter.

f.y.i.

To get an accurate count, students should identify the corner from which they begin counting.

How can you find the perimeter of this figure? Point out that this is similar to measuring around the masking tape figures. The only difference is that now you are using a standard unit of measure—inches. Have the students count the units as you trace around the figure. Once you reach your starting point, record the perimeter for the figure: perimeter = _____ inches

DISTRIBUTE STUDENT PAGE 107 to the students. Have them work in pairs to find and record the perimeter of each figure. Then ask them to compare their responses with another pair. If they find any discrepancies, tell them to demonstrate to one another how they arrived at their solutions. Encourage them to work together until they agree on the measurements.

While students are working with their partners, circulate and ask questions such as these:

- *How are you finding the distance around the figures? What is this distance called?*

- *Which figure or figures do you think have the greatest perimeter? Why do you think so?*

- *Which figure or figures do you think have the least perimeter? Why?*

- *If you were to count the units in a different direction, do you think you'd get the same number of units for the perimeter? Why or why not?*

- *Do any of the figures have the same perimeters? If so, which ones?*

- *Do you think figures have to look alike in order to have the same perimeter? Why or why not?*

Direct students' attention to the overhead projector as you show a transparency of page 107. Select four students to come to the overhead. Ask each one to trace around one of the figures, then record the perimeter in the appropriate place on the page. Students should see that, although the four figures look different, three of the four share the same perimeter. Stress the concept that different figures can have the same perimeter.

CONCLUDE THE LESSON by discussing students' ideas about the following questions: *How could we find the perimeter of our classroom? How about the perimeter of the school building? Suppose I wanted to frame a picture. I measure the distance around the picture in paper clips. Might I have a problem getting a frame that fits with that information? Now suppose I measure the picture in inches, and I find that the perimeter is 36 inches. Can I use that information to get a frame that fits my picture?*

Extension

Provide students with a few sheets of 1-inch grid paper and 6 color tiles. Ask them to first construct, then shade in, as many different figures as possible. At least one side of a tile must fit flush with the side of another tile, as in the figures on student page 107. Have students count inches around the perimeter for each of the figures they've constructed. They'll find that they are able to construct figures with perimeters of 10, 12, and 14 inches. This will reinforce the concept that different shapes can share the same perimeter. Because each figure is made of 6 squares, this exploration will also help prepare students to investigate the relationship between area and perimeter.

Student Pages

Student page 106 is a recording sheet for the masking tape figures that students measure with their feet. Student page 107 contains 4 different pentomino figures for which students find perimeters.

Assessment

Throughout the lesson, you assessed how well students understood the idea of perimeter by how they approached the job of measuring perimeters. After measuring a figure with their feet, you noted whether students understood the reason for the discrepancies in their measurements and the importance of using a standard unit of measure. As students worked on page 107, you observed them identifying a starting point and tracing the figures to find the perimeters. When students determined that different-shaped figures could have the same perimeter, you saw that they grasped an important understanding about perimeter.

NCTM Standards Summary

Students used problem solving to measure the perimeter of the masking tape figures. They not only had to find the perimeter of the figures using their feet, they had to determine how best to report the perimeter, given a variety of data compiled by the class. Students saw that the representation of perimeter can be expressed in both nonstandard and standard units of measure. They noted that there are times when it is important to use standard units to express perimeter.

Answers

Page 106
Answers will vary.

Page 107
1. 12 units
2. 10 units
3. 12 units
4. 12 units
5. B; it has a perimeter of 10 units. All the other figures have a perimeter of 12 units.

Exploring Perimeter

Use your feet to measure the tape figures.
Record your measurements on the models below.
Find the perimeter for each figure.

❶ Figure 1

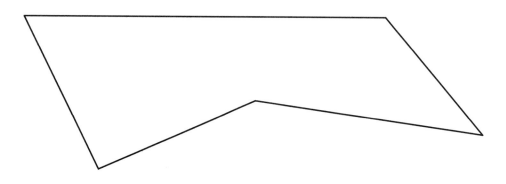

Perimeter = _____

❷ Figure 2

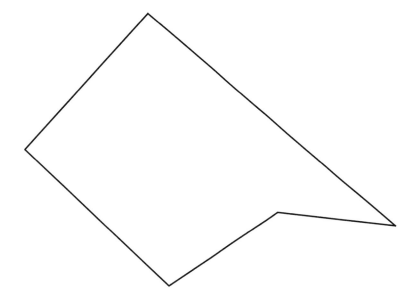

Perimeter = _____

Standard 4 Measurement

Exploring Perimeter

Find the perimeter of each shaded region. Each square measures 1 unit on each side.

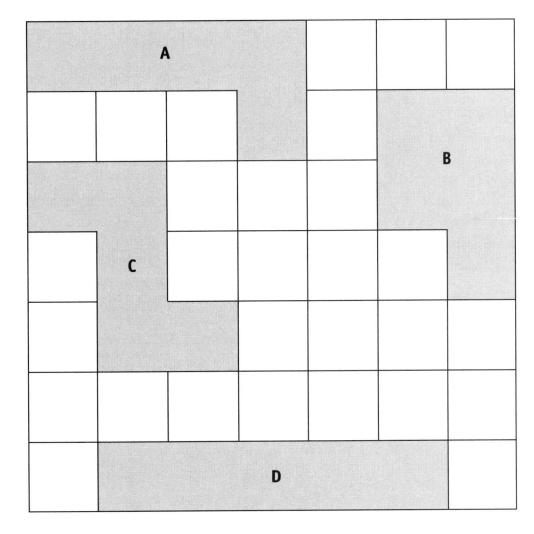

❶ The *perimeter* of figure **A** is _____. **❷** The *perimeter* of figure **B** is _____.

❸ The *perimeter* of figure **C** is _____. **❹** The *perimeter* of figure **D** is _____.

❺ Which shape is different from the others? Why?

_____

_____

_____

Investigating Capacity

Introduction

Objective → Students will estimate and measure capacity through hands-on exploration and experimentation.

Context → Students may have had some experience comparing capacity of containers. They will go on to measure capacity in standard units and to convert measurements within the customary system (cups, quarts, etc.).

NCTM Standards Focus

Working with physical models enhances students' ability to understand and work with the concept of capacity. Traditionally, students have been provided with the conversion factors for units of capacity (e.g., 1 gallon = 4 quarts) and asked to multiply and divide to answer a series of unrelated questions. In this standards-based lesson, students use measuring tools as they devise and use benchmarks to estimate the liquid capacity of a series of containers. They then measure the capacities and compare their results.

Problem Solving Working in small groups, students figure out how much water certain containers hold. Through hands-on experimentation, they devise and use methods for estimating capacity, and then find the actual measure for each container. They apply what they have learned to a problem involving a much larger amount of water, working their way up by solving smaller problems first.

Communication Students share their strategies for determining estimates within their groups and then with the whole class. They discuss the differences between their estimates and measurements and the reasons for the differences.

Connections Students apply repeated addition and multiplication strategies they have learned. In doing this, they connect their problem-solving strategies with their prior knowledge of multiplication to solve a complex capacity problem.

Teaching Plan

Materials → Student pages 112–113; 6 different-sized watertight containers labeled A–F, 3 of standard measure and the others nonstandard; 6 one-cup measures. Students will need access to a generous supply of water.

TELL STUDENTS THAT IT IS RECOMMENDED that we drink 8 glasses of water each day. Ask students, by a show of hands, how many of them actually drink 8 glasses of water per day. *How much is 8 glasses of water? How could you figure out how much water is in 8 glasses? What size container do you think you would need to hold 8 glasses of water?* Students may point out that glass size varies. Assume for this activity that 1 glass equals 1 cup.

After students have had the chance to respond to these questions, direct their attention to the 6 containers. Explain that they are going to do some experiments with these containers to help them address the questions you just asked.

HAVE STUDENTS REFER to the top of student page 112. Ask them to record the letter of each container in their estimated order, with number 1 holding the most water and number 6 holding the least. Ask students to work on their own for the moment. Explain that students will fill in the next part of the page, the actual ranking, after they measure the containers. But first, they have an estimating job.

Assemble students in 6 groups. Provide each group with a supply of water, a 1-cup measure, and 1 of the 6 containers. Again, have students refer to page 112. Explain that each group will have a few minutes to experiment with the container in order to estimate how many cups of water it would take to fill it. There's one important rule: Students may use only 1 full cup of water to help them make their estimate.

Ask the groups to listen to each member's strategy for estimating. Everyone will record his/her own estimate at the end of the time period for each container. Let students know that it's fine if group members come up with different estimates, but they should be able to defend their methods and understand each other's methods. Have students begin, rotating containers every 3 or 4 minutes until every group has worked with all 6 containers.

As students work, encourage them to take advantage of the 1-cup measure to help with their estimates, as well as to share their estimation strategies with other members of their group. Tell them that their goal should be to identify different strategies that will help them arrive at reasonable estimates.

Methods Students Might Use

- They might calculate an estimate using the 1-cup measure strictly as a visual tool.

- They might pour water from the 1-cup measure into the container and use that as a benchmark for estimating the total number of cups needed to fill the container.

- They might use the water from the 1-cup measure as a benchmark for estimating the number of cups needed to fill a portion of the container (e.g., a fourth or a half). They would then use this figure to extrapolate a more accurate estimate for filling the entire container.

Once students have recorded their estimates for all 6 containers, collect the containers, and begin a class discussion. Ask students to share their strategies for arriving at their estimates. Some general questions you may want to ask are: *Did you use the same strategy for all the containers? What strategy seemed to work best for you? Describe a new strategy you learned from one of your group members.*

NOW ASK THE GROUPS to measure the containers to the nearest cup. Have students record the actual measures next to their estimates on page 112. Once each container has been measured, have students go back to the top of the page and write in the actual ranking from greatest to least capacity. Then ask them to compare the actual measurements to their estimates.

Discuss the results. *Did any of the results surprise you? Which of the actual measurements were closest to your estimates? Which were farthest from the estimates? Why do you think this was so?*

Return to the questions you asked at the beginning of this activity about the amount of water in 8 glasses. Distribute page 113 to the students and discuss how they might approach the questions there. Then have them complete the page.

When students have completed student page 113, discuss the strategies they used to find the total for the group and the class. *How did you determine the amount of water your group and your class should drink? How did you use what you learned from the earlier activity?*

If some students are having difficulty, point out that they can approach this task with strategies they already know, multiplication or repeated addition. Encourage them to use the multiplication strategies they have acquired to find the amount of water recommended for themselves, then for their group, and finally for their class.

Student Pages

Student page 112 asks students to rank 6 containers by capacity, then to estimate the capacities, and finally to measure the capacities and compare their estimates to the actual measurements. Student page 113 has students calculate larger capacities and describe the containers that would hold a given large amount of water.

Assessment

As students completed page 112, you were able to observe the strategies they devised to estimate the capacity of the 6 containers. As they worked in groups and in class discussion, you could assess how well they explained and defended their strategies, and how well they understood the differences between their estimates and measurements. As students worked on page 113, you observed how well they were able to apply their understanding of multiplication to solve a larger problem. Their work at the end of page 113 demonstrated how well they understood larger capacities.

NCTM Standards Summary

Students used problem solving as they formulated estimates based on visual clues and benchmarks. They discussed and understood each other's methods for estimating, as well as discrepancies between their estimates and measurements. They connected problem-solving strategies with their prior knowledge of multiplication to solve first a simple, then a more complex, capacity problem. Finally, they demonstrated their understanding of capacity by suggesting and drawing a combination of containers that could hold the recommended daily amount of water for their entire class.

Answers

Page 112
Answers will vary.

Page 113
1. For Me: 8 cups;
   For My Group: Answers
   will vary;
   For My Class: Answers will vary.
2. Answers will vary.

Investigating Capacity

Estimate

1 Look at containers A–F.
Which one do you think will hold the most water?
Rank the containers in order from most to least.

_____	_____	_____	_____	_____	_____
1	2	3	4	5	6

Actual

2 Which container actually holds the most water?
Rank the containers in order from most to least.

_____	_____	_____	_____	_____	_____
1	2	3	4	5	6

3 How many cups will fill each container?

	Estimate	Actual
Container A	_____	_____
Container B	_____	_____
Container C	_____	_____
Container D	_____	_____
Container E	_____	_____
Container F	_____	_____

4 Compare your estimates with the actual measurements. Were you close?

_____

_____

Standard 4 Measurement

Investigating Capacity

❶ It is recommended that we drink 8 glasses of water a day.
How much water is that?

For Me _____ cups

For My Group _____ cups

For My Class _____ cups

❷ Look at the 6 containers you used for this activity.
What container would hold the amount of water you should drink in 1 day?
How about the amount your group should drink in 1 day? The amount
your whole class should drink? You can use a combination of the 6 containers.
Draw the containers below and label the amounts they hold.

Me   My Group   My Class

Calculating Elapsed Time

Introduction

Objective → Students will calculate elapsed time using a clock.

Context → This lesson comes in the middle of a unit on time. Students have read time to the nearest minute, and they will go on to read schedules.

Calculating Elapsed Time
• •

Learn

You can use a clock to measure elapsed time.
Elapsed time is the amount of time that passes from the beginning of an activity to the end of the activity.

Hassem started washing the dishes at 7:45. He finished at 8:15. He can count by fifteens to find how long it took him.

Start: 7:45   Count: 15 minutes   Count: 30 minutes
                                            Finish: 8:15

It took Hassem 30 minutes to wash the dishes.
The minute hand moved three numbers every 15 minutes.
Use a clock to find the elapsed time.

Remember: Every time the minute hand moves completely around the clock, the hour hand moves ahead one number.

Practice

Count by fifteens. Find the following elapsed times.
Draw pictures to show the starting and ending times.

2:15 to 2:45   5:45 to 6:30   12:30 to 1:15

Try

Juan's class has music practice at 10:45. Their practice is 45 minutes long. Show the starting and ending times by drawing a picture. What time will their music practice end?

Why is it important to know how to figure elapsed time? Write your answer.

NCTM Process Standards Analysis and Focus

The standards analysis examines how the process standards have been incorporated into the above lesson. By increasing the focus on three of the process standards, a more effective and meaningful lesson can be presented. The suggestions offered can help you to think about how this might be accomplished.

Communication Opportunities for communicating are limited to questions that elicit brief answers. Most exercises call for written responses.

Suggestion → **As students answer questions about elapsed time, have them explain the strategies they use to find their answers. Actively engage students by having them create their own questions to share with classmates. These activities will open up discussion**

More Practice

Find the elapsed time. You may use a clock with movable hands.

1. Starting time:
11:30
Ending time:
12:00

2. Starting time:
1:45
Ending time:
2:30

3. Starting time:
9:30
Ending time:
10:15

4. Starting time:
2:15
Ending time:
2:45

5. Starting time:
8:15
Ending time:
9:15

6. Starting time:
6:45
Ending time:
7:00

7. Starting time:
1:45
Ending time:
2:00

8. Starting time:
7:15
Ending time:
8:00

9. Starting time:
3:00
Ending time:
4:30

Find the ending time. You may use a clock with movable hands.

9. Starting time:
3:30
Elapsed time:
30 minutes

10. Starting time:
9:15
Elapsed time:
45 minutes

11. Starting time:
2:15
Elapsed time:
30 minutes

12. Starting time:
12:45
Elapsed time:
15 minutes

Challenge

Find the starting time. You may use a clock with movable hands.

13. Ending time:
2:00
Elapsed time:
30 minutes

14. Ending time:
3:00
Elapsed time:
45 minutes

of different ways to think about and express elapsed time.

Reasoning and Proof In the exercises for this lesson, all of the amounts of time are in simple 15-minute increments, which limits opportunities for reasoning.

Suggestion → Present situations that have varied starting and ending times. Encourage students to share

the different strategies they use to figure out how much time has elapsed. Extend thinking by having students consider strategies to determine elapsed time without using a clock.

Representation Students are encouraged to use clocks with movable hands and to draw pictures of clocks.

Suggestion → Increase students' use of clocks with exercises in which they show starting time and elapsed time. Have students create their own problems involving situations that represent elapsed time. These activities develop and reinforce understanding of the information represented by clocks.

Problem Solving Although a certain amount of reasoning is required to figure out elapsed time, problem solving is not part of this lesson.

Connections Understanding elapsed time is connected to activity schedules.

The teaching plan that follows shows how the suggestions for increasing the focus on the process standards can be implemented.

Revised Teaching Plan

Materials → Judy clocks, one for each group of three or four students; 3 × 5 cards, two per student; teacher-created sheet with four elapsed time questions, one sheet for each student

Preparation → Prior to the lesson, create four questions about elapsed time. Questions may relate to sports or daily events and should include several different time-measurement units. Consider questions such as: *Ralph started the race at 10:15, and his elapsed time was 30 minutes. What time did he finish the race? It is 3:30, and your friends have asked you to meet them at the store in 20 minutes. At what time will you meet your friends? I first saw you when you were 6 years old and now you are 9. How much time has elapsed?* Although the lesson will focus on minutes, it is helpful to offer students a larger view of elapsed time.

BEGIN THE LESSON by prompting students to think about the meaning of elapsed time. *If I tell you we will go to recess 15 minutes from now, what does that mean? If I say we will go to recess after 15 minutes have elapsed, does that mean the same thing? What do you think "elapsed" means?* Write a definition for *elapsed* on the board and clarify it with additional examples as needed.

Students are already familiar with the concept of telling time, and the phrase "what time is it?" has a clear meaning. This lesson will emphasize other aspects of time:

- What time will it be?
- How long has it been?
- How much time has elapsed?

ARRANGE STUDENTS in groups of four, and give each group a sheet of the prepared questions about elapsed time. Tell students to divide up the questions, work out the answers on their own, and then take turns discussing results with their group. Encourage and model good communication by posing a sample question. *I woke up at seven o'clock this morning, but 35 minutes elapsed before I got out of bed. What time was it when I got out of bed?* Model by thinking aloud how to use the practice clock and how you would go about finding the answer.

Distribute clocks to the groups, and allocate about 15 minutes for students to discuss and answer the questions. Circulate among the groups and help students focus on their reasoning, the problem-solving strategies they are using, and how they can better communicate the process they use to figure out their answers. *What was the first step you did in figuring this out? How can you explain what you did here? How did you know to move the big hand on the practice clock to the 3? Why did you move the big hand, or minute hand, to the 7?*

Hold a brief discussion on the different strategies students used or discovered. Invite students from each group to explain how they figured out the answers to the questions about elapsed time.

PRESENT A NEW PROBLEM that offers a starting time and an ending time. *How long is it from 10 minutes before 9:00 to 10 minutes after 9:00? How did you know it was 20 minutes? From 8:50 to 9:10, how much time elapsed?* Allow time for groups to work together to figure out how many minutes have elapsed. Then discuss the answer and listen for the strategies students have used. One method students should consider is counting 10 minutes up to the hour and then adding on the 10 minutes after the hour to get a total of 20 minutes. Present a few additional problems and follow the same procedure. Working with times in different formats and using a demonstration clock will help students develop flexibility in solving time problems.

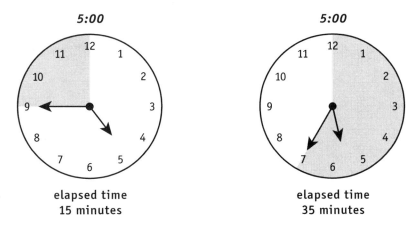

5:00	5:00
elapsed time	elapsed time
15 minutes	35 minutes

Discuss the strategy of counting up and down from "benchmark" times. Emphasize the usefulness of adding and subtracting from full hours or half-hours by modeling the strategy for the class. *To find out how much time elapsed between 4:45 and 5:35, we can count up by 5 minute increments from 4:45 to 5:00. How many minutes is that?* (15) *Then we can count by 5s from 5:00 to our ending time of 5:35. How many minutes is that?* (35) *Now if we add them together, we'll have the total amount of elapsed time.* (15 minutes + 35 minutes = 50 minutes) An alternative to counting five-minute increments would be to use larger intervals of time; from 4:45 to 5:00 is 15 minutes, from 5:00 to 5:30 is 30 minutes, and from 5:30 to 5:35 is 5 minutes. Check students' understanding by asking them to explain why this strategy works.

Prompt students to think about the same problems in new ways by asking them to set their practice clocks to a given time and then add a specified number of minutes. *Set your clocks to 9:30, and hold them up for me to see. Now change your clocks so that they show the time 45 minutes earlier than 9:30. What is the new time?* (8:45) Provide additional practice and include problems that require students to move their clocks forward as well as backwards.

CONCLUDE THE LESSON by having students create two elapsed time problems of their own and then challenging a partner to solve them. Distribute two index cards to each student. Instruct students to write a problem on one side of the card and on the other side to write the answer. Explain that problems should be stated in words and that clock faces drawn to show the appropriate time should be included for both problem and answer.

What Might Happen . . . What to Do

Students may incorrectly state problems or provide wrong or confusing answers when they create their own problems. Consider introducing procedures for checking students' work. You or an assistant can check the problems, or you might assign the role of fact checker to a third student whose job would be to help a pair of partners compose problems that are clear and correct. Then, after the fact checker signs off on a problem and answer, it can be given to the other partner for solving.

Extension

Compile a set of student-generated problems. Use these problems in an activity center or as homework assignments to provide additional practice with the concept of elapsed time and the various strategies for calculating elapsed time.

Student Pages

Students should now be ready to complete exercises similar to those on the reduced student pages.

Assessment

Both small-group and whole-group discussions in the lesson provided ample opportunities to assess the way students were thinking about calculating elapsed time. Evaluating the problems that students created and whether their answers were correct provided insight into their understanding of elapsed time.

NCTM Standards Summary

The suggested lesson shifted the focus to student involvement and communication. The small-group work and class discussions gave students many opportunities to engage their reasoning and communicate their strategies for solving problems about elapsed time. Representing times on demonstration clocks and in sketches helped students to reinforce their understanding of the lesson concept. Finally, composing their own problems allowed students to synthesize what they learned about calculating elapsed time.

Standard 5 **Data Analysis and Probability**

AT THE THIRD GRADE LEVEL, data analysis and probability include a lot of work with different graphical representations of data and probability concepts. Our lessons are derived from these important topics. They include a lesson on probability, a lesson in which students create bar graphs, a lesson in which students interpret information contained in a line graph, and a lesson on reading a pictograph.

Three lessons model how the process standards can be used to teach content. A fourth lesson is a hypothetical textbook lesson that we have revised to be more standards based. These four lessons do not represent the entire curriculum, but rather provide glimpses of how, with a more concentrated effort to incorporate the process standards, better mathematics teaching and learning can be achieved.

In one lesson on probability, students try to predict the number of cubes of each color in a bag. This lesson is driven by the process standards of reasoning and proof and communication. Students have to use the information from the random samples to determine the contents of the bag.

Another lesson we have chosen has students creating bar graphs. This lesson is driven by the process standards of communication, representation, and problem solving. Students read and transfer data from a table to a bar graph, and discuss and explain how they set up their graph and how they decided what scale to use.

A third lesson we have chosen asks students to interpret information contained in a line graph, and draw conclusions from the data. Through the process standards of communication, representation, and reasoning and proof, students gain a better understanding of the kinds of information that can be displayed in a line graph, and how the information is interpreted.

The hypothetical textbook lesson we have chosen to revise is one in which students read and interpret information contained in a pictograph. A typical lesson generally presents a superficial lesson, asking for simple information from the graph. Through better incorporation of the process standards of communication, representation, and reasoning and proof, students are asked more about pictographs, and why they might be preferable to another type of graph.

Standard 5 Lessons

Exploring Probability

Creating Bar Graphs

Interpreting Line Graphs

Reading Pictographs

Exploring Probability

Introduction

Objective → Students will determine which set of data is most likely to produce certain results.

Context → Students are able to state outcomes for simple probability events. This lesson will serve as an underlying concrete experience for later lessons in which students will learn how to express probability in a precise way.

NCTM Standards Focus

The study of probability begins with students recognizing that some events may be more or less likely to occur than other events. They understand that some things could never happen, and are, therefore, impossible; other things are sure to happen and are, therefore, certain. They begin to look at certain data sets and random samples, and conclude which samples are more likely to come from which sets. Concrete activities that the students take part in can solidify these concepts and lay the groundwork for the more precise understanding of probability that will come in later years.

Problem Solving The lesson takes a problem-solving approach. Students are given a sample and challenged to decide which of several data sets the sample is most likely to have come from.

Reasoning and Proof Students decide between mathematically more and less likely alternatives. They investigate what their data tells them and make a logical decision based on the data.

Teaching Plan

Materials → Student pages 126–127 (2 copies of page 126 per student); a sturdy opaque bag containing 5 cubes of one color and 5 cubes of another color; a sturdy opaque bag containing 7 cubes of one color and 3 cubes of another color (yellow and green will be referred to in the lesson); cubes need to be identical in size and shape.

SHOW THE BAG CONTAINING 5 yellow and 5 green cubes to the students. Tell them there are 10 cubes in the bag—some yellow cubes and some green cubes. Do not tell them how many cubes of each color are in the bag. Ask students to guess how many cubes of each color are in the bag.

Give each student two copies of student page 126 to use as a recording sheet. Tell them that they will remove 1 cube from the bag, record its color, and return it to the bag. They will repeat the process ten times, each time recording the result.

Ask a student to draw a cube from the bag. Record the color of the cube on chart paper or on the board. Also have the class record the color on their worksheets. *Are you now certain that there was at least one [color of cube] cube in the bag?* (Yes.) *Why are you certain?* (Because we saw it.) *Do you know anything else about the cubes in the bag?* (No.) Make sure the cube is returned to the bag. Tell students that they will draw another cube. *Will the cube drawn be a different one?* (It might be.) *Might it be the same one?* (It might be.) *Why?* Make sure that students understand that each cube is as likely to be drawn as any other.

HAVE STUDENTS CONTINUE DRAWING a single cube and returning it to the bag until there have been ten draws. As they draw the cubes out, continue to ask them what they think they know about the contents of the bag. As the number of draws increases, students' ideas may change. Invite them to talk about how their ideas have changed and why. It is important that they understand that it may make sense to modify their ideas as they get more information. After ten draws have been completed, engage students in a discussion about the experiment.

Do we now know for certain what is in the bag? (No.)
Why don't we? We drew ten times. (We never saw all the cubes at the same time.)
What do you think is in the bag? Why do you think that?
If we drew one hundred times, could we be absolutely sure of the number of the two colors of blocks? (No.) *Why not?*

Affirm the idea that students will get a better sense of the bag's contents by drawing more times. Ask them to make a prediction about what is in the bag based on the results of the ten draws. Have them write their predictions at the bottom of their worksheets. Then show them the contents of the bag. Discuss whether or not the results were surprising and why or why not they were.

NOW TELL STUDENTS that you have another bag of 10 cubes, and you want them to do the same kind of experiment they did with the first bag of cubes. Show them the bag that contains 7 yellow and 3 green cubes. As

f.y.i.

Often students are disappointed or feel they are wrong if they don't guess the right number. Help them see that their goal is to make an intelligent guess based on the information available.

before, have the students draw a single cube, record its color, and return it to the bag. Continue for ten draws, asking the same kinds of questions you asked during the first experiment. Be sure to ask students how many cubes of each color they think are in the bag as the experiment is going on.

When the tenth draw has been completed, ask students to make a final prediction. However, instead of showing them how many cubes of each color are in the bag, tell them that they will do another ten draws. Discuss whether they think it will help them make a better prediction.

What Might Happen . . . What to Do

Often, when students are confronted with a second sample of the same data set, they totally disregard the first. For example, if the first ten draws resulted in 6 yellow and 4 green cubes, students may guess there are 6 yellow and 4 green cubes in the bag. Then, if the next ten draws resulted in 8 yellow and 2 green cubes, they will change their guess to 8 yellow and 2 green. To encourage students to think about combining the two samples, you may want to ask them how many draws were made altogether and what the results were.

CONTINUE WITH THE SECOND SAMPLE and record the results. Ask students to revise their predictions based on the total sample of twenty draws. Show the class the contents of the bag. Talk with them about how closely the sample reflects the results. Make sure you discuss the concept of adding the two samples together. *How many draws were made altogether?* (20) *How many draws resulted in yellow? How many draws resulted in green?*

Conclude the lesson by having children do page 127 as a whole-class activity. The page contains a situation and question designed to stimulate their thinking about the concepts covered in the lesson.

Student Pages

Student page 126 is a recording sheet for use during the class activity.
Student page 127 extends students' thinking by presenting a slightly different
situation from the one encountered in the class activity. It asks them to
reason about the results of a sample they did not take themselves.

Assessment

Students showed their ability to think logically about probability when they
made predictions about how many cubes of each color were in the bags.
Discussions held during and at the conclusion of the experiments provided
information about whether students understood the concept.

NCTM Standards Summary

Students engaged in experiments that laid a foundation for using a
random sample to make predictions about a data set. They used their sense
of number to make predictions about what a data set contained.

Answers

Page 126
This page is a chart for class use.

Page 127
The questions on this page are
intended for discussion. Answers
may vary.

Exploring Probability

Write the color of the cube that was drawn from the bag.

Draw	Color
❶	
❷	
❸	
❹	
❺	
❻	
❼	
❽	
❾	
❿	

Standard 5 Data Analysis and Probability

Exploring Probability

Answer the questions.

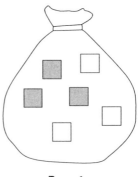

Bag 1

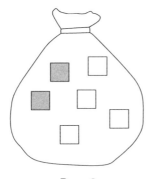

Bag 2

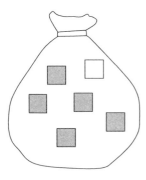

Bag 3

Karen and Armand have a mystery bag.
They drew a cube from the bag 30 times.
Here is their tally.

Unshaded	Shaded
~~THL~~ ~~THL~~ ~~THL~~ //	~~THL~~ ~~THL~~ ///

Steve and Ava have a bag, too. This is what
their tally looks like.

Unshaded	Shaded
~~THL~~ //	~~THL~~ ~~THL~~ ~~THL~~ ~~THL~~ ///

❶ Which of the 3 bags above is probably
not the bag Karen and Armand have?
Why do you think so?

❷ Karen thinks they have Bag 1. Armand
thinks they have Bag 3. Do you agree with
either Karen or Armand?

❸ They open up the bag and find they have
Bag 1. Armand thinks his guess was not a
good one. Do you agree?

❹ What bag do you think Steve and Ava have?
Why?

Creating Bar Graphs

Introduction

Objective → Students will construct bar graphs using data from a table.

Context → Students have been collecting data and using bar graphs since their primary years. In this activity, students focus on the decisions they need to make (especially regarding scale) as they construct bar graphs. Students will go on to work with other types of graphs.

NCTM Standards Focus

In the intermediate years, students refine methods of graphing and representing data. This lesson focuses on how to present data in a bar graph and how to read the graph. As students make decisions about scale, labels, and even titles, they focus on constructing graphs as a means of communicating information. They have numerous opportunities to think about and discuss how differences in their graphs affect the visual representation of the data.

Communication Given a set of data, students discuss how they might set up their bar graphs and what scales and labels they might use. After they make their graphs, they present them to the rest of the class and explain their thinking. Discussion focuses on how each graph communicates information.

Representation Students translate data from a table to a bar graph. This translation involves questions of structure, scale, and content. Students think about how their decisions affect the representation of the data.

Problem Solving Students use problem-solving strategies as they make decisions about what scale to use for their graphs and how to best represent the data.

Teaching Plan

Materials → Student pages 132–133; sheets of 1-in. or 1-cm grid paper; pencils, colored pencils, or crayons; chart paper; overhead transparency of grid paper; examples of graphs—especially bar graphs

BEGIN THE LESSON by telling students that they will be making bar graphs. They will be analyzing data and making decisions about how to display the data. Ask students what kinds of graphs they have seen and where. Ask them to describe the graphs and the information displayed. *Why might someone make a graph instead of just reporting or listing the data?* Some students may respond that a graphical representation of data can make a bigger impact. Show students examples of some bar graphs that you have collected. Have them briefly describe the graphs and the information they show. Throughout the discussion, focus students' attention on the use of graphs as communication tools.

Tell students that you are going to show them information from a survey. Discuss briefly what a survey is. Students are likely to have seen information from surveys, such as those showing the results of polls to find out what people favor or do not favor.

Present the following scenario.

> Ms. Fahlen's class polled the school's third and fourth grade parents. They asked the parents what their favorite books were when they were in the third or fourth grade. Here are the results.

Write these results on the board as you read them.

The Phantom Tollbooth	32
J. T.	27
Stuart Little	15
Ramona	39

f.y.i.

These data may be replaced with data that your class collects. Just be sure that the sample size is roughly the same as for the given data. In order to achieve the lesson objectives, the sample size needs to be large enough to force students to make decisions about scale.

AFTER STUDENTS HAVE HAD an opportunity to look at the data, ask them how they might use the information to make a bar graph. *How would you go about making a bar graph that shows the book survey data?* Tell them that later they will be making graphs of the data but, that for now, you want them to think and talk about how to make the graph. List students' ideas on the board or overhead. Encourage them to be specific in their comments. (For example: *We would need a title for the graph.*) Explain that later they will use this list to guide them as they make decisions about creating their own bar graph.

Have students review the list. Point out that many decisions need to be made before a person begins creating a graph. As the discussion continues, help the class see that good planning is essential before pencil is put to paper.

Show students the overhead transparency of the grid paper. *What should we do first if we want to make a bar graph that shows the results of the book survey?* You might want to draw a horizontal and a vertical axis for the graph. Then ask students how they would label each of the axes. *What questions do you need to think about as you decide what information to put on each axis?* The most important goal at this grade level is to have students make thoughtful judgments about where to put each piece of information. Asking questions that help students analyze the data will help them make better

f.y.i.

For this demonstration, use the vertical axis for the number of votes per book, but point out that either could be used. Later in the lesson, you may wish to have some students make the horizontal axis stand for the number of votes per book. Having them make both representations will allow students to observe different visual pictures of the same data.

You may also wish to introduce the term *scale* as students discuss the numbers on the vertical axis.

decisions. Lead them to see that there are two kinds of information that the graph needs to show—votes and books. *Where should we show the number of votes? Where should we show the names of the books?* Encourage students to see that, since there are only 4 books and almost 40 votes, it probably makes more sense to put the books on the shorter side of the paper and the number of votes on the longer side.

ONCE STUDENTS HAVE DECIDED on the orientation of the graph, ask them how they will mark the axis that will show the number of votes. *What is the greatest number of votes that you need to show?* (39) *Do you need to start at zero?* (Yes.) *Do you need to mark every number from 1–39 on the axis?* (No.) *Instead of numbering from 1–39, what could you do?* (Count by 2s or by 5s.) Again, point out that there is no single best answer. The scale used for a graph is often based on the amount of space that is available. Ask students to think about how graphs with different scales might look.

Now that students have discussed the orientation and possible scale of the graph, engage the class in a discussion about how to mark off the horizontal axis. Often students think there are no decisions to be made here, but there are. *How wide should the bars be? Should there be any space between the bars?* Ask students if they want to change the order in which the books are listed on the horizontal axis. *Would it make sense to put the books in order of popularity?* (Yes.) *Would changing the order affect the results of the survey?* (No.) Finally, ask students to suggest a title for the graph. *Are titles important? Why?*

DISTRIBUTE A SHEET OF GRAPH PAPER and a copy of student page 132 to each student. Have the students work either individually, or with a partner, to create their graphs. Encourage students to try varied approaches to making their graphs. Point out that there is no single best graph and that an important part of this lesson will be comparing different graphs to see how they communicate the information. As they work on their graphs, circulate among students to be sure that not all students are using the same scale, bar width, title, etc. You may also wish to distribute more graph paper so that individual students can experiment with different scales and bar widths.

When students have completed their graphs and answered the questions on student page 132, gather the class together and ask students to share their graphs with the class. Have students note how graphs are similar and how they are different. As similarities and differences are noted, ask students if, and how, differences affected communicating the information. Refer to the list created at the beginning of the lesson.

Conclude the lesson by assigning student page 133 as additional class work or homework. Invite students to make a list of things to think about when they create a bar graph to display information.

Student Pages

Student page 132 has questions for students to answer about the graph they created. Student page 133 gives students an opportunity to make another graph.

Assessment

Throughout the lesson, you were able to assess students' understanding as they showed their ability to create and understand bar graphs in a number of ways. They answered questions at the beginning of the activity. They made decisions about how to make a bar graph and then made it. They discussed their graphs and compared them with other students' graphs. On student page 133, they constructed a similar bar graph using new data.

NCTM Standards Summary

Students discussed the steps in constructing a bar graph and, in particular, the need to determine a reasonable scale for a graph. They created bar graphs to represent given data. In the process, they solved the problem of fitting the data on the page by using an appropriate scale. They focused on problem solving and representation to communicate mathematical information.

Answers

Page 132
1. 113
2. Ramona
3. 7
4. Answers will vary.
5. Answers will vary.
6. Yes. Explanations will vary.

Page 133
1. 119
2. 22
3. Answers may vary.
4. Accept all reasonable answers. Question might be: What is your favorite video game?
5. A pie chart might be a better alternative with only two choices.

Creating Bar Graphs

Use your graph to answer the questions below.

1 How many people answered the question for this survey?

2 What was the most popular choice?

3 How many more votes than the next choice did the most popular choice get?

4 What scale did you use? Why did you choose it?

_____

_____

_____

5 What do you think is better about using a graph than the chart?
Is there anything better about using a chart? Explain your answer.

_____

_____

_____

6 Is a bar graph a good way to show this information? Explain your answer.

_____

_____

_____

Standard 5 Data Analysis and Probability

Creating Bar Graphs

Construct a bar graph to show the data in the table.
Then answer the questions below.

Favorite Video Games from the
Third and Fourth Grades at Park School

PC Man	41
Power Turn	19
Rocket Range	36
Number Fun	23

❶ How many people answered the question for this graph?

❷ What is the range between the most popular and the least popular game in this graph?

❸ What scale did you use for this graph? Why?

_____

_____

❹ What question do you think was asked to get this information?

_____

_____

❺ Suppose the question had been, *Which video game do you like better—Power Turn or Rocket Range?* What kind of graph or chart might show that information well?

_____

_____

_____

Interpreting Line Graphs

Introduction

Objective → Students will interpret data on a line graph and draw conclusions based on the data.

Context → Students have been exposed to a variety of graphing instruments, including bar graphs, pictographs, line plots, tables, and tally marks. In their future work with data, students will construct line graphs to represent data they have collected.

NCTM Standards Focus

Throughout the intermediate years, students grow in their ability to interpret and represent data in multiple forms. This lesson introduces a new kind of graph—the line graph. In this standards-based lesson, students learn about the specific characteristics and advantages of line graphs. By reading and interpreting data on line graphs, they come to understand that these graphs are effective tools for showing change over time.

Communication Students discuss their interpretations of the data displayed in several line graphs. As they talk about the information represented, they form ideas about what is distinctive about line graphs.

Representation Students relate features of several line graphs to the details from given narratives.

Reasoning and Proof Students interpret line graphs. They draw conclusions about common third-grade experiences from the information they find in the graphs.

Teaching Plan

Materials → Student pages 138–139

TELL STUDENTS that today they are going to look at line graphs and try to determine when they are the appropriate type of graph to use. Present the following scenario. *The third grade is going to have a sports day. One of the events will be a contest to see who can throw a softball the farthest. A few third graders are having practice rounds to get ready. One of these students, Michaela, wants to see how much better she is getting as she practices. She has kept track of her best practice throws for the last five days. She wants to make a graph so she can track her progress. What kind of graph is best for showing Michaela's progress?*

As students answer this question, they will make connections to their prior experiences with graphing. List their ideas on the board and encourage them to think about how the data would look if they were represented each way. *How would a pictograph work?* (Because the data are measurements, they will be difficult to display in a pictograph. Pictographs are better for displaying data about objects that can be counted.) *Would it make sense to show the information in a bar graph?* (Perhaps; the taller bars would indicate longer distances.)

Now give student page 138 to students and tell them that Michaela decided to make a line graph. Give students a moment to look at the graph without questioning them. Then ask a series of questions to help them understand the graph. The following questions may help.

- *What is the title of the graph?* (Michaela's Best Daily Distances for the Softball Throw)
- *What does the title say the graph will show?* (The longest distances that Michaela threw the ball each day)
- *How many days are shown on the graph?* (5) *How do you know?* (The days are listed along the horizontal axis.)
- *What is written along the vertical axis?* (The distance in feet) *What does that show?* (How many feet Michaela throws the ball)
- *What is the shortest distance Michaela threw the ball?* (20 feet) *The longest?* (40 feet)
- *Why do you think the numbers on the vertical axis stop at 50?* (Possible answer: She knows that she cannot throw a softball that far.)
- *Some parts of the line are steeper than others. What does this mean?* (The steeper the segment, the greater the increase or gain.)

f.y.i.

If students are not familiar with the terms *horizontal axis* and *vertical axis,* you will want to introduce them into the discussion and encourage students to use the terms as they describe the graphs.

When students understand the structure of the graph, move on to questions about its meaning:

- *What was Michaela's longest throw on Monday?* (20 feet) *How do you know?* (The dot for Monday is at the 20-foot mark.)
- *What was Michaela's longest throw on Tuesday?* (Answers may vary between 26 and 29 feet.) *How did you decide on the distance?* (By estimating; by seeing how close the dot is to the 30-foot mark)
- *On which day did Michaela throw the farthest?* (Friday)
- *On which day did Michaela make the most improvement over the previous day?* (Thursday) *How can you tell?* (Students can subtract, or they can look for the steepest part of the line.)
- *What happened to Michaela's throws over the course of the week?* (They got longer and longer.) *How do you know?* (The line goes up each day.)
- *If field day is on Saturday, how do you think Michaela will do? Can you tell this from the graph? Can you be sure?* (Students should see that they cannot tell for sure what Michaela will do on Saturday, but they can make an educated guess of 40 feet or a little longer.)

f.y.i.

One common mistake that students often make about line graphs is that thinking that portions of the line between data points also shows information. They need to understand that the line between the points shows a trend.

What Might Happen . . . What to Do

Some students might have trouble gauging exactly where the dots lie in relation to the vertical axis. It might be hard for their eyes to track in straight lines. Help students determine between which two numbers on the vertical axis the dot lies. Then ask if the dot is closer to the higher or the lower number. Some students do well by holding a straight edge level with the dot and seeing where it crosses the axis.

NOW TELL STUDENTS the following story. *Alicia has been taking a series of timed multiplication tests. The object of the tests is to get as many multiplication facts correct as possible in one minute. There are 40 facts on the test. Here are Alicia's scores for her first five tries.* Write these numbers on the board as you read the story.

1st try	23 facts correct
2nd try	24 facts correct
3rd try	31 facts correct
4th try	35 facts correct
5th try	39 facts correct

Ask students what kind of graph Alicia could make to track her progress. Ask students what Alicia's and Michaela's stories have in common. (They are about someone getting better; they show changes over time.)

Have students work individually or in pairs to make a line graph that displays Alicia's data. Prepare them for the task by discussing the steps they will be following.

- *Exactly what information do you want to display?*
- *What title will you give to the graph?*
- *How will you show the number of facts Alicia got correct? Where?*
- *What numbers will you use on the vertical axis? Why?*
- *Where will you show the number of the try or test?*

You may want to use a line of questioning similar to what you used as the class investigated the structure of Michaela's graph.

CONCLUDE THE LESSON by bringing the class together to review the graphs they made. Focus students' attention on any differences among the graphs (such as scale). *Does each of the graphs accurately convey the information?*

You may wish to assign student page 139 for individual practice in class or for homework.

Student Pages

Student page 138 contains the line graph that students discuss during the lesson. Student page 139 presents two line graphs for students to interpret and compare.

Assessment

As they answered your questions, students demonstrated that they understood how a line graph was set up and the kinds of information it could contain. They showed their ability to read and interpret line graphs during the class activity and in their work on the second student page. You could determine how well they understood the purpose of line graphs from their discussion at the end of the lesson and from their listing of situations where line graphs are and are not useful.

NCTM Standards Summary

This lesson served as the introduction to a new kind of graph. By reading and interpreting data presented on line graphs, students learned how these graphs can be used to show change over time. Students compared several line graphs and described the information represented in them. They drew conclusions based on the graphs. In addition, they made generalizations about the best uses of line graphs.

Answers

Page 138
1. Michaela's Best Daily Distances for the Softball Throw
2. The longest distances that Michaela threw the ball each day
3. 5; The days are listed along the horizontal axis.
4. The distance in feet; How many feet Michaela throws the ball
5. 20 feet; 40 feet
6. Answers may vary.
7. The steeper the segment, the greater the increase or gain.

Page 139
1. 36 feet
2. Jonathan, 32 feet to 26 feet
3. The longest throw was 47 feet, made by Roberto on Friday.
4. Most likely Jonathan lost interest. Students might point to the fact that Roberto continued to improve whereas Jonathan improved a little and then got worse.
5. Answers will vary. Perhaps Roberto took the practices more seriously. He began throwing shorter distances and ended up improving much more.

Interpreting Line Graphs

Study this graph to see what information it gives.

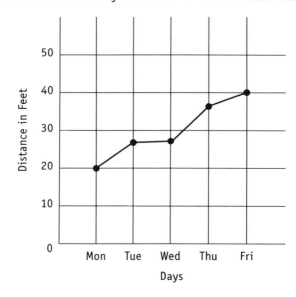

Michaela's Best Daily Distances for the Softball Throw

❶ What is the title of the graph?

❷ What does the title say the graph will show?

❸ How many days are shown on the graph? How do you know?

❹ What is written along the vertical axis? What does that show?

❺ What is the shortest distance Michaela threw the ball? The longest?

❻ Why do you think the numbers on the vertical axis stop at 50?

❼ Some parts of the line are steeper than others. What does this mean?

Standard 5 Data Analysis and Probability

Interpreting Line Graphs

Use the graphs to answer the questions.

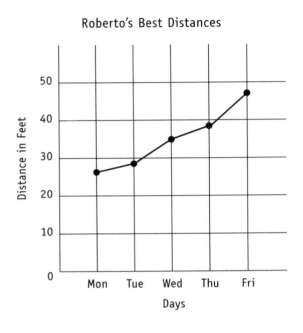

Roberto's Best Distances

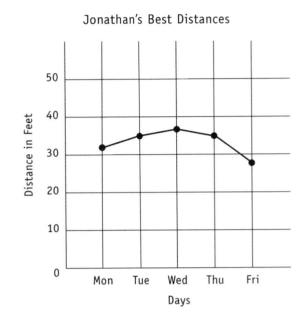

Jonathan's Best Distances

❶ How far did Jonathan throw the ball on Wednesday?

❷ Who threw the ball farther on Monday?

❸ What was the longest throw of the week?

❹ One of these students began to lose interest in throwing the ball. Who do you think it was? Why do you think so?

❺ What conclusions can you draw from these two graphs?

Reading Pictographs

Introduction

Objective → Students will read and interpret pictographs.

Context → This lesson appears at the beginning of a lesson on reading data and graphs. Students will subsequently examine other types of graphs and will make graphs.

Reading Pictographs

Learn

You will learn how to read a pictograph.

Vocabulary
pictograph a graph that uses symbols or pictures to show data
data information used to make calculations
symbol a picture in a pictography that shows a certain number of objects or things
key the part of a pictograph that shows what each symbol means

You can use a **pictograph** to compare **data** about many different things. For example, what's your favorite subject in school? Third graders had lots of different opinions.

Favorite Subject ◄——————Title

Language Arts	☺☺(
Reading	☺☺☺(◄—— Symbol
Math	☺☺☺(
Social Studies	☺☺☺(
Science	☺

Key
☺ = 2 votes

The **key** tells you that each **symbol** shows 2 votes. So ☺ shows 2 votes and (shows 1 vote.

Can you tell how many students voted for Math? The answer is 7. How can you tell?

How do you know what each symbol shows in a pictograph? Discuss your answer.

NCTM Process Standards Analysis and Focus

The standards analysis examines how the process standards have been incorporated into the above lesson. By increasing the focus on three of the process standards, a more effective and meaningful lesson can be presented. The suggestions offered can help you to think about how this might be accomplished.

Communication Students are asked questions regarding the number of symbols to use as they create a pictograph.

Suggestion → Discuss the components of pictographs and give special attention to the graph's key and the information it represents. This will increase students' understanding of how to interpret symbols when reading these graphs and the kinds of questions that can be answered by pictographs.

Try

Use the pictograph to answer each question.

1. Which subject had 5 votes?   2. Which subject had the most votes?

3. **Reasoning** If 20 students voted for Art, how many symbols would there be for Art? Explain.

Practice

Use the pictograph to answer 4–8.

Students' Favorite Ice Cream Flavors

Chocolate	𝄢𝄢𝄢𝄢𝄢𝄢𝄢𝄢𝄢𝄢
Strawberry	𝄢𝄢
Vanilla	𝄢𝄢𝄢
Mint	𝄢𝄢𝄢
Cherry	𝄢𝄢𝄢𝄢𝄢𝄢𝄢𝄢
Banana	𝄢𝄢𝄢𝄢𝄢

Key

𝄢 = 5 votes

4. Which two flavors had the same number of votes?

5. Which flavor had 40 votes?

6. Which flavor had the most votes?

7. Which flavor had the least votes?

8. How many more students voted for chocolate than cherry?

Problem Solving

9. If the pictograph did not have a key, what information would you still know?

10. Write your own problem. Write a problem using one of the pictographs from this lesson. Trade problems with a classmate and solve.

Have students develop their own questions about pictograph data.

Representation Horizontal graphs display symbols representing items graphed. A key explains what each symbol represents.

Suggestion → Offering information in more than one way broadens students' ability to understand and interpret graphs. Present graphs in both horizontal and vertical orientations. Have students examine the types of symbols used to represent data. Help students distinguish the different ways pictographs and bar graphs present the same data by comparing the two forms.

Reasoning and Proof Questions that require students to interpret information are included in the lesson.

Suggestion → Increase questions that require students to interpret data, and ask them to explain how they determine their answers. Call attention to the special features that make pictographs preferable for representing certain types of data. Focusing on the format and purpose will help students understand the advantages pictographs offer.

Problem Solving The questions presented in the lesson are quite straightforward. Problem solving is a minimal part of this lesson.

Connections The lesson makes connections to everyday life by presenting data about subjects familiar to students.

The teaching plan that follows shows how the suggestions for increasing the focus on the process standards can implemented.

Revised Teaching Plan

f.y.i.

Using overhead transparencies of the graphs offered here can facilitate the lesson discussion.

Materials → Transparencies of graphs from the text or this lesson

BEGIN THE LESSON by prompting students to examine a pictograph and determine how information is presented in this format. Use a pictograph from your text or make a copy of the one presented here. *What specific items or categories are represented? What do the symbols represent? How do you know?* (This information is explained in the key.) *How can you tell which item or category has the greatest representation? How can you find the total number of each item or category represented? Why do you suppose the symbols used were chosen?* (Generally, the symbol is representative of the subject matter.) *Suppose that this graph did not have a key. What information would you be able to tell about the categories or items represented?* (You would be able to tell that there are twice as many mystery books as history books, but you would not be able to tell how many books there are in each category.)

Pictograph

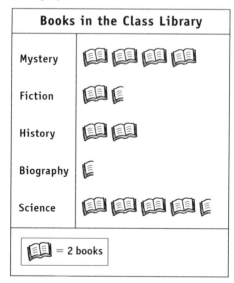

Bar Graph

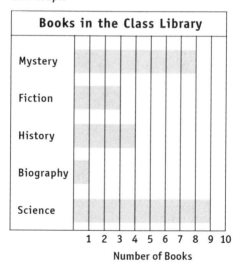

Next, help students interpret the information in the pictograph by posing specific questions. Engage students' thinking by having them record their answers to each question. Then discuss their answers to provide immediate feedback and foster understanding.

How many fiction books are in the library? (3) *How do you know?* (There are $1\frac{1}{2}$ book symbols, and each symbol stands for 2 books.) *Which category has fewer books than fiction?* (Biography) *Compare the number of fiction books to history books.* (History category has one more book than the fiction category.) *Which category has the most books?* (Science) *If there were 10 history books, how many symbols would be used on the pictograph?* (5) *Why?* (Since each book symbol represents 2 books, 5 book symbols would be needed to show 10.) *Which type of book is most popular?* (The pictograph does not provide this type of information, and so this question cannot be answered.)

Discuss how to interpret information when a portion of a symbol is used. *If a symbol of a book represents 20 books instead of 2, how many books would $\frac{1}{2}$ of the symbol represent?* (10 books) *What about $\frac{1}{4}$ of a book symbol?* (5 books) *How would 30 books be represented?* ($1\frac{1}{2}$ symbol). Depending on their grasp of simple fractions, you may wish to involve students in an activity in which they use manipulatives to find answers to the preceding questions.

DISPLAY THE BAR GRAPH next to the pictograph. Students should be able to explain that in the bar graph, there are numbers along one axis and that each bar represents a category; the bars extend to represent the appropriate number. In the pictograph, on the other hand, a symbol indicated in the key represents a given number of items. To find the number for each category, it is necessary to count the symbols and add or multiply by the value they represent.

Why do you think someone might choose to create or read a pictograph instead of a bar graph? Help students understand that data in pictographs get attention and look more friendly than other types of graphs. Explain that pictographs are especially well suited to purposes in which it is more important to present a general impression and get attention than to display precise information.

CREATE AND DISPLAY a second pictograph with information presented in a vertical format, or use the one pictured here. Have the symbol used in the key represent a value greater than that used for the book graph. Ask questions similar to those asked for the book graph to ensure that students know how to interpret the data presented in this pictograph. Be sure to connect to students' computational skills by asking them to determine and then compare the numbers of students favoring each of the sports represented.

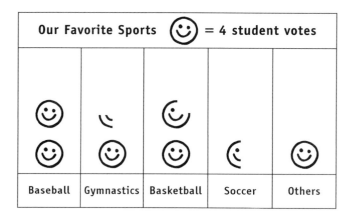

CONCLUDE THE LESSON by using one of the pictographs already discussed and altering the information it contains by adding symbols to some columns and changing the value the symbol represents. Present the altered pictograph to the class and instruct students to work in pairs to create questions about the graph. Challenge students to create four questions that are significantly different from one another. Write several question starters on the board: *How many more . . . ? Which category has twice . . . ? How many fewer . . . ? How many in all . . . ?*

What Might Happen . . . What to Do

Students may need additional support in writing questions. One option might be to have students make all four questions slight variations of the same question. *How many liked baseball? How many liked gymnastics? How many liked basketball? How many more liked ____ than ____?*

To help students develop a more varied set of questions, as well as the broader reasoning required to create them, work with students to recall some of the questions you posed about the graphs used in the lesson. Point out differences between the types of questions asked. Having students recall specific questions you have posed and using them as models to generate question starters will help students formulate their own questions about the altered graph.

Have students exchange their completed questions with another pair of students. Allow several minutes for questions to be answered, and then ask each pair of students to present one of the questions they answered to the class.

Student Pages

Students are now ready to complete exercises similar to those on the reduced student pages.

Assessment

The lesson provided ample opportunities to assess students' abilities to read and interpret data on a pictograph. Students were able to demonstrate their understanding by answering specific questions that connected to the data, its representation, and the computational skills needed to generate answers. The closing activity gave students the chance to reveal how well they grasped the lesson content by prompting them to write and answer their own questions.

NCTM Standards Summary

Engaging students in a discussion about pictographs and the different formats in which data can be displayed enabled students to communicate their own ideas about the representation of data. Analyzing the different types of questions that can be answered by examining a pictograph assisted students in learning how to interpret data and formulate their own questions about the data. The lesson also introduced students to graphing as a flexible representation of data by asking them to focus on pictographs with different symbols and orientations. Students compared the information that can be interpreted from a pictograph with a bar graph that displayed the same data. Throughout the lesson, students used reasoning and proof as they worked to interpret and analyze symbolic information in different contexts.

Create Your Own Lesson

THIS LAST CHAPTER IS DESIGNED TO HELP you develop your own lessons in which you can comfortably incorporate the NCTM standards with your teaching style. We start with a list of questions to help you focus on factors to consider as you begin to organize a standards-based lesson. Then, we model the process used to create a lesson, as you are walked through the thoughts and decisions one person used in developing a lesson.

The questions listed here are meant as a guide, a starting point; they are offered to get you thinking about how to develop your lesson, what material to cover, what steps to follow, what questions to ask. Hopefully, these questions will trigger additional ideas that you will add as you go along.

Write down the ideas that come to you as you read each question. There may be questions for which you don't have an immediate response, but don't worry; as you begin working on your lesson, ideas will come. Start by selecting the general content area. Think about the concept you want to develop. Then, narrow in on an objective for the lesson. Be specific and be realistic. What does meeting that objective mean? Is there a skill that students should be able to perform after completing the lesson? Are there questions they should be able to answer? How will you determine that the objective has been met?

Next, think about the process standards: Problem Solving, Reasoning and Proof, Communication, Connections, and Representation. What approach will be effective in helping students understand the concept? Try to envision how the lesson will flow, how it should begin, what activities and questions will be included, and how you will assess learning. Understand that there can be several ways to successfully teach any lesson. As you begin to design your lesson, new ideas will come and you will be able to refine your thinking.

Focusing Questions

1. What content standard is to be addressed? What concept within that standard is to be developed?

2. What information do the standards offer about this content?

3. What do students know about this content? What don't they know?

4. What is the specific objective of the lesson? What should students be able to do at the end of the lesson?

recognize	identify	define
review	compute	classify
compare	create	other

5. What kinds of questions should students be able to answer when they complete this lesson? What skill(s) should they be able to demonstrate?

6. What resources are available to develop this concept?

references	textual material
manipulatives	supplementary material
colleagues	student knowledge

7. What can realistically be accomplished in the time allowed?

8. Which activities and process standards can best help develop the key ideas?
   - using drawings, charts, diagrams (Representation)
   - focusing on symbols (Representation)
   - conducting small-group/large-group discussion (Communication)
   - having students gather and analyze data (Problem Solving)
   - thinking through relationships and explaining them (Reasoning and Proof and Communication)
   - finding ways to prove thinking and verify solutions (Reasoning and Proof)
   - extending/building on former knowledge (Connections)
   - integrating the concept with another discipline (Connections)
   - relating math to its use in the real world (Connections)

9. What questions will focus students' thinking on the concept and help guide learning?

Developing the Lesson

EVERY YEAR THERE IS AN EVENT in my class that makes a lot of students very anxious. It's the unit on the multiplication facts. This topic is very important to students, to parents, and to me. Many students see this unit as the gateway to the mathematics of the intermediate school years. Parents are always asking me how their children are doing with "the facts."

I think I generally do an acceptable job of teaching multiplication facts, but I want to work on how the children view this task. My goals are to have them be less anxious and to see the facts as a challenge they will be able to meet. I want to develop a kick-off lesson for learning multiplication facts, to get the class moving in a positive direction that will lead to success.

I've learned a good deal during my years of teaching that I can put to use with this first lesson. I know that while most of my students really want to do well, some things seem to get in the way. A lot of my students get defeated psychologically. They think the task will be too difficult and that makes it difficult for them. Often, they are inefficient in the way they work; they practice the facts they know and don't concentrate on the ones they don't know.

There are strategies and patterns that students can use to help them learn the facts. I want to make these a focal point of the unit to help students memorize the facts. If they can't remember a fact, these strategies can be used to figure it out. I think this is very important. Otherwise, when students don't know a fact, they guess, and if they guess wrong, an incorrect answer might be reinforced as the correct one.

Here's what I want this lesson to accomplish: I want my students to see that they have a challenge ahead, a challenge that will require work and commitment to meet, and that they will have to put in time and effort. I want them to know that this is a challenge they will be able meet. I also want them to realize that learning the facts is an individual thing; it's not a competition to see who will learn them first. I want them to feel assured that my focus will be to help everyone to succeed.

In order to be aware of strategies and patterns they can use to help them to learn their facts, I want students to think about the numbers. I want them to see relationships among the numbers. I want them to understand that recall with a certain amount of speed is important, but that speed will come with practice. First, they will need to know the facts.

As I LOOK TO THE PROCESS STANDARDS for guidance in putting this lesson together, I see that communication will play a large role in this lesson. I will need to communicate some very important points to students about how to learn the facts. We will need to communicate about the strategies and patterns. As we work with these strategies and patterns, we will be making connections to things the students have already studied such as addition facts and mathematical principles—like the commutative property. Finally, I see reasoning playing a large part in learning the facts. Students will need to use reasoning skills to apply the strategies and techniques that will help them memorize these facts.

I'll start the lesson by telling the students that they are going to be learning the multiplication facts. I'll make several points.

- Learning the multiplication facts will require hard work and it will be challenging.

- I believe every student can be successful. The class will be using patterns and strategies to help make the job easier.

- Learning the facts is not a race. The only competition any student has is with him- or herself.

- Speed is important, but not as we start out. Speed will come from working with the facts and having lots of practice. The more we work and practice the facts, the faster we'll get.

The next thing I'll want to do, is demonstrate something that I've seen before; something that does a great job of driving home the points that I made about the task being doable and how using strategies can help. I will display a multiplication chart on the overhead. We'll take some time to review the chart and how to use it. This review should be easy since the children have used similar charts for addition and subtraction. I'll explain that the chart contains all the facts that they are going to learn and I'll ask them to determine how many there are. (There are 121 facts in the chart.) I will ask them if they think that's a lot to learn, and I assume they will respond positively. It seems like a lot to learn to me!

×	0	1	2	3	4	5	6	7	8	9	10
0	0	0	0	0	0	0	0	0	0	0	0
1	0	1	2	3	4	5	6	7	8	9	10
2	0	2	4	6	8	10	12	14	16	18	20
3	0	3	6	9	12	15	18	21	24	27	30
4	0	4	8	12	16	20	24	28	32	36	40
5	0	5	10	15	20	25	30	35	40	45	50
6	0	6	12	18	24	30	36	42	48	54	60
7	0	7	14	21	28	35	49	42	56	63	70
8	0	8	16	24	32	40	48	56	64	72	80
9	0	9	18	27	36	45	54	63	72	81	90
10	0	10	20	30	40	50	60	70	80	90	100

I will tell them that, in the next few minutes, we will be reducing that number of 121 facts to a manageable size. I think this will be a dramatic step, one that will have a very positive effect toward putting them at ease. It will prove to them that strategies can help immensely. We will start by cutting, in half, the number of facts the students need to learn.

We have already studied the concept of multiplication. Students know how to make an array of 3 × 5 and one of 5 × 3. I will review this with them and ask how knowing that 5 × 3 has the same product as 3 × 5 could help them learn their facts. I'll ask them to look again at the chart. I'll start by drawing a diagonal line from the upper-left corner of the chart to the lower-right corner. I'll point out that this line falls on the products of numbers multiplied by themselves (2 × 2, 3 × 3, 4 × 4, and so on).

Next, I will show the students that on either side of this diagonal line, the chart is a mirror image of itself. I will ask them to locate the products for 3×5 and 5×3, note how they are the same, and note how they lay opposite each other on either side of the diagonal. Once students learn 5×3 they know 3×5. Understanding this can cut the number of facts students have to learn almost in half. I will encourage students to see that, if we subtract the 11 square numbers along the diagonal from the 121 facts in the table, 110 facts remain. I will help them see that they will only need to learn, about half of those facts, since there are related facts on either side of the diagonal. Half of 110 is 55; 55 plus 11 makes 66 facts—66 facts to learn.

Now, I will ask my students what other facts they already know. I will ask them about 1×0, 2×0, 0×1, and 0×2. Students will see they know that multiplying any number by zero is zero. I will shade the row and the column that include multiplying with zero.

Next, I will ask them about any number multiplied by 1, and 1 multiplied by any number; they already know that any number times 1, and 1 times any number, is that number. I will shade in the corresponding row and column.

Then, we will move to the 2s. I will ask them: *What is 1×2, 2×2, and so on.* Twos are easy; finding the product of any number and 2 is the same as adding the number to itself. Students already know this from the addition facts. I'll shade in the row and column that include multiples of two.

Next, we will look at multiplying numbers by 10. Again, students will see that they know those products or they can make a rule to get the answer almost immediately. I will shade the row and column.

After shading all the facts that they know, what will be left is the square portion of the table from 3×3 down through 9×3 and over to 3×9, and from 3×9 down through 9×9. This square is cut by the diagonal. There are the 7 square numbers along the diagonal, plus another 42 facts that are unshaded. Since each unshaded fact has a partner, or related fact, students will only need to learn 21 facts. Those 21 facts, plus the 7 square numbers along the diagonal, make a total of 28 facts altogether that students need to learn.

In a very short time, we will have taken the number of facts that need to be learned from 121 to 28. I will let the students know we will start working on those 28 facts and will review what we know tomorrow.

×	0	1	2	3	4	5	6	7	8	9	10
0	0	0	0	0	0	0	0	0	0	0	0
1	0	1	2	3	4	5	6	7	8	9	10
2	0	2	4	6	8	10	12	14	16	18	20
3	0	3	6	9	12	15	18	21	24	27	30
4	0	4	8	12	16	20	24	28	32	36	40
5	0	5	10	15	20	25	30	35	40	45	50
6	0	6	12	18	24	30	36	42	48	54	60
7	0	7	14	21	28	35	42	49	56	63	70
8	0	8	16	24	32	40	48	56	64	72	80
9	0	9	18	27	36	45	54	63	72	81	90
10	0	10	20	30	40	50	60	70	80	90	100

Reviewing the Plan

I feel that this lesson will accomplish the objectives I set for myself. It uses the standards and my teaching experience to help me get my classes started on the right foot for learning the multiplication facts.